The Complete Poems
of
Ursula Vaughan Williams

and a short story
Fall of Leaf

Edited, with an introduction, by Stephen Connock

Albion Music Limited

Published by Albion Music Ltd,
a division of The Ralph Vaughan Williams Society
(Registered charity number 1017175)

First edition 2003

ISBN:0-9528706-5-7

Printed in England by The Basingstoke Press

Ursula Vaughan Williams

Introduction

Ursula Vaughan Williams was born in Malta in 1911. With a strong military background, her early years were inevitably spent on the move. Leaving school at 17, she attended finishing school in Brussels where she was able to visit opera, theatre and art galleries establishing the interest in music, literature and art which she has maintained to this day.

In 1932, she had the opportunity to become a student at the Old Vic Theatre Company. In the same week that she auditioned at the Old Vic, she became engaged to Captain (later Lieutenant-Colonel) Michael Wood. They married in 1933.

Ursula had begun writing poetry at the age of ten. The earliest poem in this collection is *The Mountaineer*, written in 1927. Her first published collection appeared in 1941 under the title *No Other Choice*. Further collections were published in 1943 and 1948. Ursula has also written four novels, three of which have been published.

Following the death of her husband, Michael, in 1942, Ursula's friendship with the composer Ralph Vaughan Williams deepened. They married in 1953.

Whilst Ursula Vaughan Williams does not belong to any school of poetry, the influence of certain writers can be detected in her poetry. She had discovered Yeats in 1925-6, and his impact can be noted in the stylish and subtle imagery which distinguishes her work. It is, perhaps, Thomas Hardy who is most frequently remembered when reading Ursula's poetry, especially in the range of formal structures adopted, in the flexible metres and in the evocative and atmospheric tone.

Her poetry appeals to musicians: it has been set by over 30 composers, one of whom said:

"There is a beauty to it. It is very sensitive. She can capture moods and ideas in a few words or lines. Above all, the words are evocative, and stimulate a musical response."

Around 250 poems are included in this complete collection. They deal with the big issues of life - love, old age, war, jealousy, sadness, death, illness, the environment - in a way which can be both profound and moving. It is poetry which is often inspired and always evocative. It is hoped that this volume of poetry will bring to Ursula Vaughan Williams the recognition which she so richly deserves.

Stephen Connock MBE
Chairman, Ralph Vaughan Williams Society

Preface

When the *Collected Poems* of Ursula Vaughan Williams were published in 1996, they brought back into public circulation many superb poems which did not deserve to be out of print. Interest in the book stimulated Ursula to make available to me a number of hitherto unpublished poems, written over a period from 1930 to the mid 1980s, which I have included in *The Complete Poems*. They seem to me to capture something of Ursula's sense of atmosphere, romance, insight and humour. These new poems are grouped at the end of the volume under the general title *Miscellaneous*. Some of these were written for Ralph Vaughan Williams, some for special occasions, and others relate to Ursula's work as a librettist over many years.

Also included is the first publication of one of Ursula's short stories, *Fall of Leaf*. She is rather proud of this story, which once again shows many of her strengths as a writer, particularly her insight into human emotions and her ability to explore complex facets of personal relationships. It is a memorable story which effectively concludes this book.

Finally, the opportunity has been taken to correct or amend many of the poems included in the first edition. This editorial work has been a pleasure. Special thanks to Joyce Kennedy, Ken Blakeley and Cynthia Cooper for their help in the proof reading of this book. It is hoped this further edition of Ursula's poetry will consolidate her reputation as a poet and writer of major importance in the twentieth century.

Stephen Connock   *September 2003*

List of Illustrations

Contents

No Other Choice

(1941)

Ursula Vaughan Williams

The Quarry

Along the green banks by the waterside
the fishers sit and idle summer through,
gazing at silver floats that nod and ride
above the gleaming cool where fishes slide
elusive under sky-reflecting blue.

Out on wide frozen marshes speared with reeds
'til winter sunset the numbed fowlers lie
masking net and trap with rush and weeds,
waiting to lure some wanderer where it feeds
weary from flight across the snow-brimmed sky.

I'll sit a patient year to take a thought
listen and wait until the bait is taken
and out of depth and height the creature's caught
and closed inside the cage of words I brought.
Then from this tranced wait and watch I waken

knowing that somewhere meaning goes astray,
once shut in language the essentials fade
like the heaped silver catch that lay
filling the angler's basket at the end of day
or the limp spoils of the fowler's trade.

Under the summer bank smooth water lies
where fish are flickering between reed and stone.
Brown winter sleeps beneath its icy skies
and high as cloud or wind the migrant flies
remote as thought whose words are still unknown.

Mountaineer

High, alone in this desolate world of the winds
where clouds quiescent lie on hills below,
I watch the ice, that like a girdle binds
the still white beauty of the mountain snow,
and shadows burn blue flame in each crevasse.
The afternoon streams slowly by, and night
follows that yellow hour, when mass on mass
the hills below stream to the plain in light.

The Naturalist

Solitude's life for you, the marvelling eye
accepting all it sees, and seeing all.
Where we go blind with hope, or lost in memory,
you listen till the intonation of a call
tells you of hunger, fear, or deep content
of busy creatures, earth dwelling and small.
Wing spread, wing shadow, beaks so curved or bent
name the bird to you, dappled markings tell
the moth, faint tracks the way an otter went.
To me an empty world, to you a spell
so deeply laid, that you are firmly bound
by sight and hearing, taste and touch and smell
to loved and living ground.

That thoughts are a continual surprise

Thoughts breaking like ridged waves
out of the unknown darkness of the mind,
a moment all the substance is displayed
and just as fast withdrawn, and left to find
only some small shells lying on the sand
and cold spray salty in an open hand.

As secret as the wind, wider than sky,
shut in this skull, my mind will lie
and let thoughts break like waves until I die,
as waves, slip through the hands
leave but a curled trace on the sands
and so return to their deep secrecy.

The Enchantment

There is no refuge while the senses live,
so you shall grow at last into a tree;
then, to the earth your autumn leaves will give
colours that shall return, in flowers for me.
So thought shall end, and, unafraid of chance,
instinct will shed your leaves or open buds each day.
You will need nothing then, you need not dance
to find an ecstasy, nor read nor pray,
but self-sufficient shall your branches spread
increasing splendour, deep between earth and stone
your roots find comfort; and then it shall be said
'how beautiful a tree has Daphne grown.'

Aloe

(The plant that flowers once
in a hundred years)

Seek and you shall find
no answer of music to the thought
or of colour to the sight;
knowledge is only bought.
Stone holds the form disguised
that you would bring to light,
and so we learn, surprised
that only in the mind
can the aloe flower
in half an hour.

The Gothic Angel

O those far staring eyes
that seem to look with man's imprisoned sense
and more than mortal certainty, to find
wisdom's a planet native to the skies,
are stone, are blind.
It is the maker's searching and his impotence,
though to a sculptured beauty he has bound
his spirit's hope, and sureties of his mind,
and set them in the clouds, remote from quarried ground,
those eyes are stone, are blind.

The Archaeologists

Excavations by Moonlight
The moonlight spreading across the hill
sheds a reflected glow on the heaped-up chalk
that we dug today, and where you walk
a long black shadow moves like a pointed quill.
Many juniper bushes are crouching around the pit,
but the gleaming chalk has given up its dead,
small heaps of broken pottery, brown and red,
an antler shaped as a pick, and the skull that stares at it.

On Digging up a Skeleton
In this skeleton I cannot recognise
wise man or fool; yet had I seen
the quiet body lying in candle light,
having come too late to read the living eyes
I should have known the man that he had been
at sight.

Marked by the spirit and the burning mind,
flesh mirrors self with small disparity,
and face and hands show all life's habits clear.
Is individual then to flesh confined?
Only an outline of mortality
lies here.

The Burial Place
Here at our feet the treasures lie,
stillness of death informing stone and gold,
once honoured flesh the little dust they hold
so secretly.

And one day other men will find,
deep drifted in forgotten dust of years,
the words we made to cradle hope and tears,
to free, to bind.

After Fishing

The contemplative silence descends
like shadows lengthening darkness on the grass.
Enamelled leaf from leaf sharply divided
is in the stream repeated
when the last brilliance of the sunlight lends
gilding to colour, that as it shines will pass,
for day is ended.

Along the riverside mist rises,
and the cold smell of dew, of water at night,
drifts with a wind that stirs the hanging willows
along the water meadows,
till a white owl, flying low, surprises
crouched waterbirds that chatter in their fright;
repeated silence follows.

Sight

Within oneself deserts and mountains are,
cactus desolation and polar night,
landscapes electric blue becalmed on white,
till outward vision answer the inner sense
more absolute than shadow, as intense
as movement poised in stillness, and aware
of wings alive for flight.

Prologue

Flesh to this meeting moves,
aware and sensual,
threading between casual
moments and things, to loves
predestined by some choice
made with both mind and voice
but blindly . . .

Mind, like a bird in air
or comet, scars with flight
the distance, in delight
to find such freedom there,
but will not stare behind
to trace the path we find
blindly.

'I am two fools I know
for loving, and for saying so . . .'

I

Seven o'clock: all night my heart has counted
yesterday's kisses over,
remembering yesterday morning, when I went as a lightfoot lover,
that now am hunted
by more love than I can bear.

II

But past is past, and will not come again.
I thought myself bound-free, secure from pain
of any other love than that I have,
no echo even met the love you gave,
and so it was till the last moment came
I caught your fire, and cannot staunch its flame.

III

Ah when will this long weary night have end?
When will my heart its load of trouble spend?
But empty hearts aren't lighter or more wise,
and sorrow shines, dark lanterns in the eyes.
There's a choice here, until we choose and go
the chosen way, neither of us will know
whether we're fools or not, though time will show.
Only the crying of the arms we know, and guess
the body's everlasting loneliness.

IV

The stars are netted in the branches high
where the wind stirs
soft leaves murmuring together, and the dry
leaves of firs.
Fall evening, fall all darkness on us here,
branches bend down,
close this blue midnight round us where
we drown.

V

There are no debts in love
when you discover
your own heart's all that matters,
your own heart that scatters
its folly everywhere,
and reads in the eyes of a lover
the thoughts it would find there.

VI

Closed in your arms, all peace possessing,
sleep, like darkness round us folding
heart and spirit you are holding,
complete beyond all longed for blessing.
Made whole at last, what should this peace inspire,
O Phoenix, dreaming in a sleep of fire?

VII

Hands, give him all the measure of my love
surer than any word.
Eyes, be deep pools of truth, where he may see
a thought more whole than constancy.
Heart, in his keeping, be at rest and live
as music and silence meet and both are heard.

Night

I

When in my arms you lie
heavy with sleep
I am more content than a deep
green river between high banks moving certainly.
Seen in the water trees are dark against the sky,
the reflecting water flows past, and I, to sleep,
drowned in green water, happily, deep
in warmth, in sleep,
and you asleep in my arms, contented lie.

II

Beauty, that rare and migrant bird,
has spread its wings round me tonight
alone and quiet in the candle light.
Why did you go? The night is still,
the half moon lightens all the hill
and patterns leaves across my feet.
O sad that we can never meet
here in this moment, between light
of moon and candle, both burn and are obscured,
and beauty is a rare and migrant bird.

'Old wives a-sunning sit. . .'

Time's not an enemy to friends,
though words that kindle words grow less
and change the tenses.
But kindness lingers in the deadening senses
and nothing ends,
though two that talked all night until the day
will sit together with no words to say
in easy silences.

The Changed Landscape

I remember a time
when this was a hayfield,
simple and pastoral as a nursery rhyme.
But since they planted pines,
and the trees have grown tall
in dark straight lines,
the simple flowers have gone.
It is dark under the branches,
I am afraid to walk here alone.

This girl is dead

(From the French of Paul Fort)

This girl is dead, she died at break of day,
this girl is dead, dead while with love she lay.
They lay her down alone, alone in her array
they lay her down alone, shrouded alone to stay.
They have come back to the fields, the fields at break of day,
they have come singing gaily, like any other day.

Lazarus

We waited in the quivering heat for his return.
None of us had seen a miracle before, but we believed
in the man, and his accredited acts. We were not deceived:
he did return.

We had thought, simply, that we should all rejoice,
gathering round him, strangely unchanged by the days
he had been dead in the dark, then go on our various ways
having heard his voice.

But when he came it seemed cold as night, and we fled,
having seen fear in his terrible eyes, and great despair.
We could not break into his isolation, nor did we dare
hear what he said.

But his sisters stayed unguessing, being blinded by joy,
they took his hands and kissed them, and led him inside.
In a day or two they forgot he had ever died
or had changed since he was a boy.

The Swans

Place

The sea is bound in ice, grey, white and grey,
where the wide stillness holds no hope of spring
and light's a measure shorter than the day,
and cold is part of stillness: winds that bring
the snow are here imprisoned and must stay
frozen to earth, powerless to blow away
the lightest feather cast from a migrant's wing.

Here the swans gathered, resting after flight,
but from this desolation they are gone.
When the late morning touched their wings with light
they vanished southwards. When the winter's done
they will rest here returning, but till then no sight,
no sound will break this still unshadowed white
where the pent wind and prisoned wave are one.

Lullaby

Listen, listen . . . the snow is falling
hushing sound in whiteness,
brushing grey glass lightly as a feather,
listen, listen, falling feathers heaped in lightness
measure the winter out in this white weather.
All the swans have flown together,
high above snow they fled in brightness,
soft as feathers snow is falling,
listen, listen . . .

Elegy

Now they will lie till the unpitying spring
looses the ice and snow, sinew and bone,
and sweeps white feathers from each outstretched wing,
the swans are gone.

The dying swans who sing, who sing to Death,
a song ascending as their wings are stilled,
till earth at the last flutter of their breath
is echo filled.

have lived to the full measure of their flight.
But these were netted where they came to rest
tired from the icy air: the colder night
froze on each breast.

Here, in the world abiding, beauty lies:
for unguessed pain, life broken, not a word,
only the legendary death, the visionary eyes,
the singing bird.

Alms

Sorrow, be metal for the mind of man,
not like white transience of the winter frost
that binds in pain forgotten soon as lost,
but to endure, as furnaced metal can.
Let the racked body and remembering mind
in some long lasting form their passion show.
Sorrow defend us, for us seek and find
hope to transform the blinded face of grief,
that from a thorn a flowering tree may grow,
the hurt give alms, the unwounded take relief.

To *the* Historians

Can you, with clear and practised vision
see beyond cities that will be destroyed?
or hear, louder than guns' derision,
a future freedom singing in the void
sprung from a war's decision?

We, urgent to know our hopes returning,
fear broken body and the desolate town.
How should we guess, beyond a city burning,
a harvest springing from the grass cut down
not singed and brown?

Death holds a mirror to distort our sight,
pain excludes wonder, grief dulls the eager mind.
Where do we follow? Migrant birds in flight
have never seen the lands they surely find:
blind lead the blind.

Soliloquy

Still in the valleys the echoes cry aloud
after my heart among these silences,
echoes of footsteps and shadows of palaces,
pearls in the water, mirrored towers white and proud,
and green branches.

Now I must learn the customs of solitude.
An eagle's shadow flies along the ground,
the pillared clouds crumble without a sound,
no trees speak to the wind with the voice of a multitude.
What have I found?

I have found hills where sand and rock and time
become each other, build and disintegrate,
endless mutations of their primal state
in colours of desert and shadow, lava, fireopal, lime,
dark shale and slate.

Look from this height by moonlight - down and far
the world's rim curves no boundary to space,
the mountain's shadow darkens all earth's face,
and out beyond burns star and further star
I cannot trace.

And so they burned before the waters fell,
mist, dew and rivers filled the earth's deep sea
whence life rose winged and growing; ancestry
common to men and dragon. Bird, fish and animal
share mystery.

The past, all future then, from darkness came
as rivers rise from earth, and wandering find
a final sea, so journeys all mankind,
hopeful or fearful, wise man or fool, their journey is the same;
man travels blind.

Careless of us they made their living world:
thoughtful for us, some, with bequeathing hands
left wiser laws to rule their conquered lands;
for merchandise, for islands, in vision their ships sailed,
their buildings stand.

With time's wrecked ships and effigies of queens,
past days and hours unalterable lie,
and heir to all the past, I, living, cry:
'Spend all the heart's possessions, until Time quench
        the daylight green
in memory.'

Love in its brilliance and its desolation
is like the dancer's music, lovers are bound
within their passion; lost while music's sound
masks all the world beyond as stage and decoration,
a dancing ground.

They are the living, full of resurrection,
the lanterns set wherein the flames are bright,
illumination and surrounding night . . .
two worlds alive together. What life springs from
destruction?
What dark from light?

Waves that have strangled and drowned will never cease,
and fire forever blackens flesh with pain,
mirage of suffering builds each scene again,
the merciless imagination tormented turns from peace,
repeating pain.

But when there's no choice left, no chance to save,
strength matches pain, courage beyond despair
looks through the mastered flesh death will not spare,
but looks not back to comfort us, whose flame, the breaking
        wave,
or the beast's lair.

Or in stillness, alone without respite,
who can look back to comfort when the past
is all resolved? When sight is clear at last
for morning, or more darkness than depth of any tidal sea
where light is lost.

Now turns to never, the climber's empty hand
leaves the last hold, and clear his shadow lies
like a long track known to both heart and eyes
through time and place, by wood and water, harvest and
barren land
whence echo cries.

Fall of Leaf

(1943)

Finding

Stranger to silence, listen, be comforted,
for sound and silence, daily interspaced,
meet here in sight.
Colour and sound are muted both by night:
bird after bird ceases from song and flight,
still, blue and deep,
distance outstretches to the sky, and shadows steep
in quiet the trees and grass, all houses, dark with sleep.
See and be comforted.

Here all past summers lie. Here their increase
spreads wider branches. Though they only lease
a lifetime's beauty,
time cannot touch the human memory
that flowers in you, lights for your living eye
known and unknown,
until you too, listening, have grown
one with the silence of all summers done
in the night's peace.

Looking back

The past possessed and bound in stone Lot's wife:
Orpheus turned back to a dead love from life.
And I look back, for both of these am I
and on the future their dark shadows lie.

Lot's Wife

If I turn back to stare upon the flames,
it is because the city, in my mind,
still holds my home, my days. The names
of square and street and garden still I find
conjure the place into sight's memory
till I am sure of their reality.

It is like this after a journey's done;
when one comes home and shuts the door
thinking of places left behind, the sun
still shines on them though left a week before,
and still the petals scattered on the grass
lie, as if days remembered never pass.

Reality is here; is the wind
that blows a smell of fire across our way;
it is the stones with which our way is lined;
the dust that chokes the tears, turns grey
the dark smooth hair: sorrow would turn it white
for grief is frozen; here's but a fool in flight.

To go, one takes provision for some days,
thinks first in terms of food and covering,
maps for the journey, choosing less known ways,
and small and special treasures that will bring
a thought of home into some far strange room
now waiting empty as an emperor's tomb.

Then we are gone. Turn at the corner, see
for the last time that curtain blowing white.
Part with a wrench from domesticity,
the copper saucepans that were always bright,
the linen piled and smooth with years to wear,
and cupboards filled, and flowers everywhere.

Sunlight half filled my room, and in my glass
behind my face, the shadow of a vine
traced its carved leaves, and there I was
a woman still. All that I saw was mine,
and like my tree I too had roots and spread
a sheltering presence. Now I too am dead.

The city lies smouldering ash and dust.
In its destruction fell not only walls,
the skill of builders too; and then you must
think of the labourers. The city falls,
the architect's design as well as stone
breaks into rubble, and creation's gone.

My heart is with the women whose lost days
were spent embroidering curtain cloth and sheet,
men who worked silver in fantastic ways,
those who made sandals for the dancers' feet;
painters and gardeners, all the craft and skill
of hands that follow and translate man's will.

As real as the sunlight when we fled
the winter's snow will cover arch and stair,
till grass shall hide the city and its dead
and the doors opening on nothing there,
and the black ashes of destruction,
the body that will seek no resurrection.

If I could turn and see the smoke still blown,
still rising from the cities of the plain,
stone tears would fall upon a face of stone,
my body know the ruined cities' pain.
If I could turn and see . . .
stone tears would fall.

Orpheus

Singer of life, whose voice confines us all
in the enchanted bondage of one sense,
Death will listen if you choose.
Use your power, none refuse
pleasure drawn out in fine threads of sound
beyond the limits of intelligence.
Sing to the twisted spirits underground
until your lover rise as flowers rise:
possess their hearing till they bless your eyes;
for if you cease
and look within her heart to find your peace,
again she dies.

. . . and I

This stone was grooved to fit a hand.
I hold it now by the same grasp
its maker knew.
I found it on the fresh ploughed land
where, till this year, wild grasses grew.
What flowering summers lie between
these furrows and that green,
those fingers and my clasp?

Guess at the maker's questioning
where future, beyond working hands
grew in his eyes.
What did he see? The chipped stones bring
so little knowledge to the wise;
yet this is my inheritance,
made by skill, found by chance,
here on this common land.

The stone is mine; his vision less
than Time, reaping his sowing still,
gathers and scatters.
But I look back to him and guess
the past and not the future matters:
what's now makes then; turn to the past
for prophecies that cast
their shadows on my will.

Once of one substance, man, fish, bird
went separate ways, chose earth and air,
water, not fire;
and for their separate lives they herd
in confines of their own desire,
accepting life and finding death;
none but man spends his breath
making words, making care.

From a lovely face take years
till simpler beauty shows again;
imagine youth.
So, take from earth the marks it wears
of man's long groping after truth,
his harvesting and granaries,
his roads and palaces,
and walls against his fears.

The animals make lair and den;
the birds inherit songs and die;
the silent fish
move in dark seas, again, again
repeating beauty; while men wish
and search to know, possess and find
Earth cannot hold this mind
that seeks infinity.

As if the choice were half in vain,
rejected fire with lightnings fills
man's thought and dreams.
His gods with fiery splendour reign,
like light their inspiration streams:
and from his dark imaginings
angels ascend, their wings
blaze beyond mortal hills.

Yet he is held and clothed and bound
by the long past all creatures share:
sinew and sense
still bind life to its chosen ground
and task; us with obedience.
My hand inherits all the past,
and, while the senses last,
this chipped flint that I found.

Procris

Procris is lying at the waterside,
the yellow flowers show spring, the grass is green,
before a gentle wind the thin trees lean
towards the rushes, the rushes to the tide.
She will not see
the green spring turn to summer, summer go
in a long golden dusk towards the snow,
with eyes so lit by love that everything
burned, flowed, grew, blossomed, moved on foot or wing
with the guessed rhythm of eternity.
All her hope and will
flowed from her unavailing
and she knew darkness, as her eyes know now
shut to the daylight, and despair prevailing
she saw no way to go.

I

The Institution

'Ten thousand stood round me, yet I was alone. . .'

Gathered here, like swallows before migration,
the old and poor come without possessions,
sit on benches, idle in the sunlight.
Spent flesh is withering on their bones,
muscles contracting, heads bent with a weight of days
that will not pass unless sleep stays
to be a day's companion.
They, like the swallows, have left their summers behind:
their words in a hundred soliloquies remember
name and place, child and hope and summer,
gossip at doorways, faces at the window,
women who were themselves coming and going
each at the centre of some world built of small possessions.

Each from her world of having comes alone
to wear the anonymous garments of charity,
to sleep in narrow beds close to each other,
to wake to another day of waiting
though the swallows have gone already
across the bright autumn sea.

II

The Fortune Teller

Three-coloured cards between us lying
to me are emblems. What to you,
who look at meaning as I look at colour?
Where are you searching? Days like treasure lie
heaped in your hands; I choose;
you see the common boundary of tomorrow fall.
The careless past will someday be completed:
is it completed now within your sight?
Bring back, like gold washed from fabulous rivers,
promise fulfilled and knowledge growing wise,
clues for the maze, prophecies for despair;
build me a city, guide me to a door,
for this the cards are scattered on the floor.
What do you see?

Spider

Out of herself the spider draws a thread
and runs from leaf to leaf to spread
traditional and intricate
the pattern of her web: makes her estate
upon the air.
She watches with a black unsleeping stare
her net spread in the currents and the tides of day
for winged prey.
Then, having fed,
she wraps the shrivelled bodies of the dead
bumble bee and bottle fly
in twists of web as delicate
as the unopened calyx of a flower.

There are voices

There are voices speaking to each other everywhere
across the silence. Sounds hurrying, meeting, parting,
words made for comfort, fear, expedience, chance,
voices heard for the last time, and echoes starting
that will repeat a phrase for ever in the heart.
So many words traversing silence, threading the air
netting me in their meaning and their care.

Although he looks beyond the cloud and light
a shipwrecked man is bounded by the sea,
waves spring and die across his field of sight.
So I listen, listen as he will stare,
I for your voice, and he remembering land
beyond the waves' inhuman and unchanging dance.

Valentines

I

Too early for the daisy or cherry stones to tell
if he loves me, or loves me not, or loves me far too well.
Too early for the knot grass to answer yes or no,
so what shall I do till the daisies grow?
What shall I do till the cherry's red
to know if he'll ever say the things he's never said?

Why wait for the cherry? the buds are hardly green.
Why ask the daisy petals to guess what he may mean?
Ask him, St. Valentine, ask him to tell
if he loves me, or loves me not, or loves me far too well.

II

Women will always wear their beauty for you,
whatever they have, like a rose in the hair
or a silver dress. They will move like dancers
between low burning candles and the first light of day.
You will see the smiles caught in a dark mirror,
a scarlet shoe on the stairway, a footprint on the grass,
but not the living creatures as they pass.

This curl, this silver shoe, this rose is mine,
but I am here inside the gay disguise.
Find me, find me ... the rustle of stiff silk,
masked laughter, thin hands with emerald rings and yellow fans
hide me from you. Love is more mad than blind
when masks and shadows are all that he can find.

III

Tipped with gold or sharpened lead,
with silver feathers for a wing,
Love's arrow curves through space to sing
quivering in the heart, and shed
there its wealth of care and grief,
there its joy beyond belief.

Though the dart be lead or gold,
fledged with feathers of a dove
that shows your destiny in love,
like the pilgrim's staff, behold,
between the spearhead and the wing
leaves unfold and roses spring.

Tired

Sleep, and I'll be still as another sleeper
holding you in my arms, glad that you lie
so near at last.
This sheltering midnight is our meeting place,
no passion or despair or hope divide
me from your side.
I shall remember firelight on your sleeping face,
I shall remember shadows growing deeper
as the fire fell to ashes and the minutes passed.

The Effigies

Who in their senses would envy the effigies?
Who, stepping from bright and coloured day
into this monochrome of dark and grey,
holding the summer's flowers, would be here and stay,
envying the crusader where he lies,
or wish to change this coloured silk for smooth stone draperies?
Each statue holds a truce with time. Time-fearing love
might easily ask no more than this unchanging state,
carved of one stone to be together and disparate
while centuries across horizons move.
O hope unknown
to share the unread inscription and forgotten date,
the formal gesture of prayer, the silence of stone.

There must be time for grief

There must be time for grief:
work has its hours, and love, food and sleep
take their due, and days go by
measured by necessity.

Drawn curtains show the morning,
the clock pointing the cue for entrance into day;
the dance has started, the dancer cannot stay:
the intricate discipline is beginning,
the sun burns time away.

Close the curtains, shut out night.
All day, all day
grief has eluded, darkened the corners of the mind,
edged a word, shadowed a hand.
If there was time to receive it I might understand,
might look into it as a mirror: in its reflection find
that the past recalls its love, is somewhere, whole and secure,
as travellers' cities, never revisited, remain
just as they were before.

But it is night again,
and it is sleep that takes my hand.
Tomorrow there must be time enough for grief.

Fearing Apparitions

Why fear a ghost, shrink from a night of dreams?
Neither is what you knew:
or, if the shadow of the thing it seems,
it will be only gentleness to you.

My part of death

I

Words spoken lightly, words used every day,
familiar currency of touch and look,
so much belonging, familiar and expected,
has come to an end. I or any one else can say
the same things over again. You never may.
What have I heard and remembered? What neglected?
Searching the past for you, I look
at so many places, so many moods together,
the action flowing towards this brink, this break, this going away.

Death has so many powers I did not guess:
changing to-day, filling the past with strangeness,
making it more than it was, and the present less.
This is the water of petrification, flowing and turning to stone,
binding the past in a stillness I never suspected;
your words and gestures become unchanging, everlasting.
Stranger that was well known.

II

The houses we lived in are haunted more than remembered.
If I stood at a window surely I should see
both of us living there still, sitting in firelight;
moving, flickering flames lighting yellow walls,
warming tables and chairs, the colour of my dress,
pointing your heavy ring with flame; our idleness
full of content.
And I, the watcher outside, could not doubt the night
enclosed in the walls, in the past's serenity,
but would question my flesh and blood, not memory.

Which is the ghost? Had you or I looked out
from the warmth of then into the night,
would we have seen me curious and alone
looking through empty windows, and known
ourselves but shadows left inside a room?

So you are everywhere we ever went.
A word, a look, a quarrel all remain
bound to the road, the room, the well-known lane;
and I too listen, answer, quarrel all again,
and find our lives scattered across the south.

III

I've seen from flight at evening, small between earth and sky
horizons change from land to breakers everywhere,
the valleys narrow and the hills grow small,
the prehistoric track, the Roman wall,
shadows of trees and towns diminish.
Our journeys, ventures, idlenesses crowd
into a smaller space, grow less and vanish,
for Time's wings drive me though I backward stare.

IV

Time's measured for the eyes by day and night,
the changing moon, harvest and hour-glass,
flocks of small birds gathering for flight,
bonfires and heathfires, and the glow-worm's light,
leaves growing dark and shady, frost that can surpass
the leafiest summer with white shadowing white.
Four other senses share the world with sight
watching the seasons pass, and centuries pass.
Year after year I shall hear wind and rain,
touch petals fallen from the almond tree,
walk in the snow, or shelter under leaves
while distance grows between us. No harvest sheaves
will turn green in my hand, be seed again,
nor sun stand in the sky because of me.

V

Though the newborn have all custom and usage to learn,
they hold, like the seed of corn, the fruit of trees,
promise and fulfilment. They inherit
all man's dependence on the earth and seas,
the journeys and the trophies of the spirit.
The newborn are sheltered by pity and tenderness;
who can comfort the dead, be gentle to them in their strangeness?
It is the living who learn
that earth makes individual ashes earth.

VI

Where shall I find the resurrection?
All the ceremonies for the dead
are paid in the currency of life,
the silver coin, stone jar and hunting knife,
folded draperies, wafer of bread,
the dirge and promise of the requiem.

The metaphors for death are night and sleep,
as if the ashes were scattered seed
sown in autumn for the future's need
and not for earth to dissipate and keep.

The dirge and promise of the requiem
stand between us and the dead, who are unknown,
who are strangers, having left all that we knew them by.
Is the seed barren? or what flower has grown?
Where shall I find the resurrection?

VII

We could have been old together,
argument stilled to tolerance, and content
grown a deep root from which our days would spring.
Trees grown for centuries together
have branches interlaced in long consent
where the birds stay to sing.
The separate branches make a shade together
and when the summer is spent
the leaves fall one on the other as coloured as the spring.

Firewatching

I

Moment, my certainty, where all the senses live,
sand runs so quietly through the hour-glass,
how shall this grain be held?
What is the evidence added together to give
sharp contours to the moments as they pass?

To live now is to look back. Touch what you will,
cup, plate, fine silk or necessary bread,
a hundred histories are there, for still
we inherit more than living from the dead,
more than a shack upon a barren hill.

Small, in the shadow of the enormous past,
a man descending a mountain might look down
and stare across a continent; the vast
territories, the cornlands, forest and town:
he by the spring, at the edge of the snow could see
the river widen to its estuary.

But we at the river mouth, loitering by the quay
where ships come loaded from some foreign land
with corals and bright birds and pearls and mystery,
look outward still, touch with an eager hand
this evidence of more discovery.

Measure the mountains by man's sight,
the earth by journeys, and the sea
by voyages to where the unknown lies,
by common currency of day and night;
bring home into this moment history,
be harvesters my ears, my hands, my eyes.

II

The summer night stirs with the lightest wind.
I can remember summer nights like this,
when under my window branches stirred,
and the cold scent of flowering may and earth
made my hands grope for all spring's promises.
And nights when moonlight shone on rivers, and the bridges
circled the water with reflected arches:
we walked in the dew, and others walked there in dancing dresses
pale as white clematis and phlox by the water.

O landscapes with remembered figures.

The lightest wind stirs in the summer night,
the siren fades above the darkened windows,
and beams of searchlights wheel about the sky
searching for death among the constellations.

Brighter than stars and guided by calculations
as delicate as the mechanism of a clock,
shells burst; explosions echo to the ground,
we count the alternate flash and sound.

Here we are tented in the brilliance of disaster,
here falling walls and the thick dust of plaster
carry it downwards, downwards into comprehension,
measuring huge pinnacles of hate and fear
by inches of destruction in our sight.

III

A city is burned down, the streets are gone;
Familiar spires no longer soar above,
white in the morning, where starlings cluster
turn in a cloud to settle and come to rest
wing after wing rustling like leaves of trees
against each other on a summer night.
The trees are blackened by fire, the branches gone,
the ashes are heaped and white.

Travellers, though never in Time returning,
remember cities once known, remember by heart,
and so are the streets we knew remembered,
streets where we walk with our shadows,
where other ghosts once walked in meadows.
Our city is part
of the heart's landscape. Build as they will
till the new skyline's familiar, the old like a dream returning,
a city unlighted at night remains for us still.
But when we die, the last survivor gone,
then, in the ancient fields, it will lie ruined, alone.

IV

Here are the empty houses and the shuttered,
the ruins where the rosebay grows
through gorse and bramble on the cellar stairs:
the theatre where we watched the acrobats
swing in the arc lights above the arena,
they were dancers, like moths in lamplight, feathers in the air.
And now the siren strings its web of sound over the city
fading away, and further warnings crying
silver and faint for miles and distant miles
from street to street, all across the country,
across the continents.
You cannot hear where the sound ends,
or know where there's a boundary to fear.

V

Fear has a thousand different forms and faces,
a devil mask for every eye
that stares from the empty place on the pillow,
or is heard in footsteps hurrying by
from unknown places in the night to unknown places.
There's no propitiation that can change
this hour to day, bring morning near
to count for one more day all that is loved.
Now is for ever to those whose hope is fear,
and sleep and daylight distant and as strange
as resurrection.

VI

Nothing is itself alone: the child that held a shell
wondering at the smooth and midnight blue
tapering to grey, and saw for the first time
the shallow curling edge of the incoming tide,
saw all his summers in the advancing waves
by all the seashores he would ever find
as certainly as memory can return
to those long tamarisk-shadowed days,
sea-sounding nights that held the child sleeping.

Though Here and Now are fetters to the limbs,
Now is ephemeral and will be lost
between this breath, this heartbeat, and the next;
and Here's not mine, but territory shared
with all the past and all to come hereafter.
A Roman helmet and a burnt-out plane,
with my lost ear-ring and the child's shell,
are silt in the river, dust on a buried hearth:
so stars still seen, symbols of constancy
thinned out to ash and vanished long ago
although their brightness still pierces our nights.
Destruction bears its long inheritance of weeping.

VII

Remember the legend of Adam under the tree of knowledge
that was man's shelter by day, where he watched the stars
through the bare branches in the winter solstice,
and followed the arch of the branches to make a bridge,
and gathered the fallen leaves to clothe his nakedness.
We have cut down the trees and squared the branches
and built a city from the sapless wood.
How should we, in our generation, have understood
what Adam knew with the stolen fruit in his hand?

Need for Speech

(1948)

Need for Speech

Joy needs no words, larks singing over meadows,
swallows at evening, dipping from sun to shadows
touching the water's stillness under willows,
all peace and all content are clothed in light
closed in the crystal globe of sight.

A prisoner's anguish teaches his hand to write
scratched on the dungeon walls, or on the night
the words cut from his heart are diamond bright;
brighter than life lie his remembered meadows
and quieter than sleep the shadows.

The Old Actress

She's the fantastic princess of her dream,
round her bent shoulders there's a threadbare coat,
an agate brooch means jewels at her throat.
The waters of the moat that rock and gleam
where boats and swans drift on a captive stream
that keeps the world away, her pension can provide,
shillings and pence the silver-copper tide.
Her dyed red hair, her thin yellow face
nodding above the fire, still bright
where flames lend her rusty curls their grace,
are withered colours of brocade and lace.
On the floor a maze of beetles crawl,
embroidered dragons on a palace wall
could never glare so, stare so, flicker, run,
as in this cellar darkened from the sun.
Sitting alone I see her, but she's not alone,
she's dancing with two ghosts, Flattery, and Success,
with death perhaps three dancing steps away.
Her clock shows morning at the end of day,
six hours late it ticks with measured pace
like high-heeled footsteps in the paths of space.
The tattered firelight has almost gone
and darkness lies like velvet on her dress.

A *boy dreams of birds*

(for Johannes)

A boy dreams of birds
till they float above his head,
wings canopy his bed,
brush his fingers and knees,
garlanding trees
grown between dark and light
where horizons of morning spread
to receive their flight:

while he kneels by a pool
where swans with folded wings
listen as he sings,
curved necks bent to his hand
outflowering from land
fingers curved to a shell.
Here he can understand
all he must tell.

'Cold symmetric wings,
warm breast, my silver dove
never flutter or move
from hand or dream;
dark room, still seem
my wing-leaved grove
by a swan-shadowed stream,
no day cage my birds.'

The Peasant at her Window

She sits by her window listening with folded hands
while village sounds gather like swallows under eaves:
children play where a water trough stands
shadowed by fig trees; a boy with a bunch of leaves
drives cows in from meadows, cow bells ringing;
women call to each other from their open doors,
brown hay-makers ride home on the high hay-load singing,
and perpetual river murmurs to its shores.

She sits in age's stillness, orchard stillness,
the yellow ripeness of September days,
while evening turns to shadows, there she stays
her square brown hands learning their idleness.

Penelope

Certain parting does not wait its hour
for separation; too soon the shadow lies
upon the heart and chokes the voice, its power
drives on the minutes, it implies
to-morrow while to-day's still here.

They sat by firelight and his shadow fell
for the last time she thought, black patterning gold
sharp on the firelit wall. So, to compel
the evening to outlast the morning's cold
dawn by the quayside and the unshed tears,

she took a charred twig from the hearth and drew
the outline of his shadow on the wall.
'These were his features, this the hand I knew.'
She heard her voice saying the words through all
the future days of solitude and fear.

Wilders

I

The cottage stands alone
on a high pebble bank,
greenly overgrown
where brambles rank on rank
beat against the door
trying to go in:
and brown spiders spin
elaborate curtains that fall
grey on the blackened wall
while grasses creep through the floor.

The garden has grown wild,
its flowers revert
and are reconciled
with feathered weeds that skirt
the broken wall.
Bent fruit trees stand
in this no-man's land
knee deep in hay,
wind blows the seeds away,
and apples lie where they fall.

II

This is a quiet stretch of river land
where streams divide pastures, ditches are never dry,
where herons nest in willows and stand
waiting in shallows and pools all day for fishes
and cattle doze among flowering rushes.

This is a quiet stretch of time, an idle day:
watching is living, slow hours flow by
bringing content, carrying away
only silver ripples, cloud shadows on water
or a heron's feather, the colour of pewter.

III

To go inside the ivy-guarded door,
sit on stairs, climb to the upper floor,
to count the four small rooms and wonder
who lived here before,
is to long to stay, to shelter for ever under
this slated roof, listen night and day
to sighing branches, flowing river
that carries time away.

The hearth remains, sign of man's possession:
fire, burn to-night, welcome my succession;
shadows move where only darkness came
since dispossession.

I celebrate home-coming with a flame,
for man returns to where he lived before,
articulate sound shall measure the green silence
and sleep space day from day.

IV

All night trees mutter to each other,
dark yew to ash, sweet walnut to spiced bay,
codlin apple, bird cherry and near against the wall;
leaves rustle and stir, bindweeds smother,
thorns tear darkness, branches sway
to a gusty wind that eddies as water eddies
restless, restless, brushing sleep away.

 All night the house speaks to itself, or me,
mortar flakes between bricks, falls on the splintering floor,
nails loosen in window frames where briony tendrils sprawl,
the hearth quenched the fire that only burnt sombrely:
rain should have climbed the stairs, wind unlatched the door,
or time let in sky and weather, forgetting
that man was tenant here before.

V

   Go, no place remains
   for man's pains,
   for fire or hearth,
   or ordered path;
   plaster from lath
   must fall.

   Go, who comes shall find
   the windows blind.
   The roof tumbles,
   the wall crumbles,
   nettles and brambles
   cover all.

   Go, the walls shall soon,
   like a cocoon,
   break to release
   the prisoned space;
   and the lost green peace recall.

VI

Morning lies golden on thick dewy grasses,
herons fish for ever
in pools of silver,
willows stand with their roots in shadow,
cattle graze in the ample meadow
where mushrooms lie as white as stones.

Briar and bramble have entered the house,
climbing briony
outstrips dark ivy,
walls are trellised with bindweed and creeper,
trees are closer, silence deeper
and I shall go as the others have gone.

Jess

I

A mile beyond the road Ash Corner lies,
a lane leads to it, downhill, through the woods
where the young trees are barely shoulder height;
under them, in the spring, primroses light
the hellebores' dark leaves and cool green hoods
bowed over windflowers, cold as winter skies.

Jess lived enclosed by woods, by bird's-eye panes,
closed in the green shade of a rainy spring
when the rain drips all day from eaves and sills,
drips from the tasselled chestnut flowers and spills
into the hollow tulip leaves, while everything
grows thick and rank in gardens, fields and lanes.

All afternoon in her tree-darkened room
she danced between the mirror and the fire,
her shadow large and her reflection small;
she watched them both keep measure on the wall
moving as if they knew she would not tire
remembering music in the firelit gloom.

She danced alone because she longed to be
where others danced: because she could not read
or sew or daydream being filled with discontent.
She must outstrip the day, dance the unspent
hunger of her heart away; because her need
drove her lightfooted onward, where she could not see.

'Solitariness and my hurrying thoughts
meet and be one; accept this way of living,
learn satisfaction from enchanted sight,
let cold snow crystals and the globe of night
pattern tranquillity, so forgiving
this anguish of the creature trapped and caught.

I am self-trapped, so for what capture grieve?
I came here gladly, where else should I stay
but in a husband's home? and yet when he is near
there's nothing more to say. He is still dear
but separation grows in us. From day to day
we cherish tenderness in which we half believe.

Or is it idleness that saps my mind?
No: these rooms shall answer for my care,
our garden shows the work of busy hands;
but discontent twists dark and heavy strands
into the pattern of this life I share,
in which I walk as if dull, dumb and blind.'

Her intricate dancing steps cannot outwit
her heart's despair or the slow afternoon.
Rain falls silently, roof gutters run with streams
and drip perpetually. A broken bird's egg gleams
enamel blue on earth; the yellow cat called Moon
puffs out his fur and goes to sniff at it.

The door bell broke her thoughts, so she could run
to welcome someone, postman, country neighbour,
a voice at least, a break in heaviness:
she darted through the house, glad that her yellow dress
would be for someone's eyes, opened the door
to all that sense and truth and reason shun.

A stranger who had lost his way stood there
asking to shelter from the rain;
he'd missed the short cut by the water meadows.
As he spoke his voice touched all the shadows
and drew them round him, even the heavy chain
behind the door shone, stripped of centuries' wear.

He watched her see this as he spoke. He said,
'No things ill-done cannot be smoothed away,
things used made new. A second chance is given
to those who'll trade with me. No bargains driven
but simple give and take; you choose another way
and pay my price. The starving must be fed.

The starving fed - with their own flesh indeed -
the sleepless rocked to sleep - in their own dreams -
the restless, dull, unhappy, made content
taught to turn back upon the way they went.
Time is my hour-glass, up or down it streams
following pleasure, satisfying need.'

She understood his offer, knew she'd cast
the shadow of her disappointed heart
on joy and tenderness so withering them.
She saw her life too clearly to condemn
more than herself from whom she could not part
knowing how present comes as sequel to the past.

'What have I done with life that I should be
ready to change all that was dear so easily?
What have I done with all my nights and days
to see them coldly, with a stranger's gaze?
How can I hold them, shrunk so utterly
from all they were when they were part of me?

Ready to change all known, change day to day,
quietness that should clothe old age
not bind me in frustration. Let me live
as I consider living, and I'll give
my immortality, a distant image
of unendurable continuity, away.'

Then suddenly the stranger seemed no more
than a chance passer sheltering from the rain,
and the rain ended as he turned to go.
A small mark on her wrist remained to show
he'd touched her there, marking the insane
bargain his, and sealed; her wish secure.

Look inwards or look downwards where a stream
flows, but leaves the water-darkened face
seeing its own reflection clear as glass;
gaze mirrored there to watch the water pass,
it mars no detail, touches no curl or lace
nor stirs the deep enclosed, enclosing dream.

A falling leaf can break reflection, show
the river bed before it shapes again,
lie lightly as enchantment on five senses,
or sound's brief pattern upon silences;
time's measured on eternity in vain;
beneath your mirrored eyes the waters flow.

II

Her yellow cat was her familiar
gazing at darkness with moon-glinting eyes,
gazing at her with calm indifference,
both animals, both without innocence,
held together by inescapable ties
the devil's gift, to each peculiar.

She learned the spells of change, to say,
'Go into hare.' The bones closed in her hands
and changed to white-flecked paws, meanwhile her sight
showed only monochrome, her feet were flight
across the downs to where the gallows stand
half rotted now, and silence haunts the day.

Hay-field grass, in June knee high,
to her, a hare, tossed overhead
with sorrel and campion, the cornfields' hem,
and fan-tail barley on its knotted stem,
sainfoin and clovers white and red
were patterned for her against the sky.

She was so secret, her husband walking late
through flowering lanes, where petals on the grass
are white as daisies for the moths to find,
was blind to her, hare-like, as she fled behind
a hedge of roses, waiting for him to pass,
or cat-like crouched and slipped beneath the gate.

She'd leave a sleeping shadow of herself in bed
and run, disguised, ways overhung by fear
to a nocturnal hunting in the wood,
where beasts accepted her although she understood
none of their customs, nor came near
any companionship with them that hunger led.

Midsummer night she came along
by cottages that held deep sleep within;
roses and phlox breathed sweetness to the night
and swifts still screamed in darting flight
so high their cries seemed thin
as flittering bats' cries: nightingales in song

filled the dark trees with sound:
and honeysuckles and rose-coloured stocks,
pale as each other, still smelt of the day.
A heavy mist showed where the river lay,
and from three parishes she heard the clocks
say midnight to the midnight world around.

A man was leaning, idle, on his garden gate,
awake to watch the magical short night
change dusk to moonlight, listening, to share
the world with beast and bird. He saw the hare,
called to her and she came. His touch was light.
'Enchanted hare, why do you walk so late?

So late, so centuries late?' he said.
'You are alone, no coven on the hill
dances midsummer eve into midsummer day,
the village has lost its witches. Time blows away
even enchantments: yet it has left you still
wandering among things long dead.

Come from the beast.' So he undid the spell
as tenderly as if he took her cloak,
and she became herself and questioning.
How had he known her? 'What hare stands listening
to a bird's song, then moves as if she woke
from visions?' He laughed. 'You do not do it well.'

He led her to a small and whitewashed room
red floored, with shelves of books and everywhere
notebooks and papers strewn and spread
on chairs and tables and the narrow bed;
he cleared them for her, sitting there
he told her of the race of witches and their doom.

'Listen,' he said, 'you have your mortal years,
you have your senses and your hands,
knowledge is your inheritance and love;
you have the means for all, and yet you rove
these necromantic pastures in forbidden lands,
be wise, go home again.' She heard in tears.

'No, nothing's mine,' she said, 'I cannot make
a pattern of life; the threads unwind,
find me unready, and I do not know
even which way my eager feet will go,
only they will not stay; my heart and mind
divergent seek, not knowing what to take.'

Yet as she spoke she knew the search was done,
the stranger's face was suddenly well known
as if they had been many years together.
The window showed grey of a pigeon's feather,
a cloudy daylight, the short night had grown
invisibly to morning as they sat alone.

Grey as a pigeon's feather, grey as glass
dew lay on briar, on gossamer, on leaf,
and showed deep footmarks as she ran.
An early rooster crowed; the year's full span
blessed heart and eyes: corn grew towards the sheaf,
flowers to their fruit, as if all promise came to pass.

III

Often she would take fruit and flowers and go
down to the cottage, stay to talk and listen,
drawn to the stranger, so drawn there again
that her feet knew the way by field and lane
as well as her own garden, and would hasten
to him as certainly as rivers flow.

As the summer's self she seemed to live,
loving him with her heart's full certainty,
as if come home at last, as if a door
opened on music where silence was before,
or blindness faded leaving eyes that see,
or folded hands learned the heart's power to give.

The usual pattern of the days went on
till after harvest, when the heavy trees
bowed with their fruit, baskets full of sloes
bullace and damsons, that last of summer goes
in ragged gold, while from last flowers last bees
fetch their faint autumn honey and are gone.

She gathered the apples, russet, margil,
and crabs and pippins, some to store
some to make jam, and quinces, pears,
till the profusion that the orchard wears
spread indoors, filled the shelves, lay on the floors
or in two rows along each window sill.

And in the orchard, dusk and cold
she knew a hundred Aprils lay
between his birthday and her death,
vistas of springs she wept beneath
because not one would flowering stay
to shelter them together, young or old.

'Love so possesses me, so gilds my blood
I move in radiance, with finger points of light
touch and make new all daily things.
How can bones cage these beating wings
that stir to splendour, wake to flight,
then fold to hush and brood?

How shall I live, and not live at his side!
and how go back to those past years that lie
familiar in his memory? If I grow old
my middle years, my youth, should so unfold
run backwards, find him, stay, till I
safe in his past knew nothing could divide.'

So her imagination journeyed back
driven by passion, creating places, days,
where she was always his companion
driving all question of division
into her mind's more subterranean ways
where jealousy was waiting like a rack.

At first his words, his face, his being near
withheld her from her power as a witch;
but love unanswered shook her like a leaf
and longing quickened all her half belief;
unravelling her future stitch by stitch
she made her spell in awe and faith and fear.

She thought by making her young body old
her spirit, matching it, would stand by his,
and, without living it, have lived his past;
and so, become his counterpart at last,
grown with his life, her heart enclosed in bliss,
should wear its green untouched by any cold.

She took her mirror to the hollow night;
one future lay behind in shuttered sleep -
her husband lost, her children unconceived -
and for a moment's thought of this she grieved.
Yet this loss freed her, there was no way to keep
this might-have-been, her love must travel light.

By witches' will under the starry night
she made one moment carry years away,
and through the whirling sequence saw her face
shrivel and shrink and lose its summer grace,
a scrawl of purple veins stain her thin arm and stay,
her bracken coloured hair grow thin and white.

The devil's voice answered her anguished thought:
'Where can you go, taking the last steps only?
without the years achieved, what beauty grows?
count up your follies, think, what river flows
back to its source? My lovely, lonely
witch, fool, lover, running hare, see, you are caught,

snared in the power I gave you. In this spell
you grasped at things not yours; and now
empty, refusing, you are quite alone;
you should have lived all life, endured it to the bone,
taken its hours; for what have you to show
for seventy years that twenty could not tell?'

So morning came, with morning's busy sound,
cockcrow, and milk churns rattling at the farm,
an early wagon rolling down the lane.
She saw the silver-shining weather-vane,
she saw the golden bracelet on her arm,
she saw her mirror lying on the ground,

and walked toward the house uncertainly,
opened the door, drew back the curtains, spread
the breakfast cloth, wishing for yesterday,
touching familiar things, wondering what words to say,
because she heard her husband's heavy tread
she hid her face and waited desperately.

The Walk

You have given me autumn for ever and ever,
each leaf of October gold is mine,
pheasant-plumed plantations, fire-coloured beeches,
a living sky, a hill's unbroken line.

Year in, year out, as the season's pattern changes
sight will touch a sleeping memory
with a leaf, a colour, till it wakes and ranges
back to the clearest seen, longest remembered.

They've gathered and carted the very last of the sheaves,
gleaners gone, ploughing will soon begin,
and the hunter's moon will shine, gales blow all the leaves
in a whirl of yellow across the fields.

Nightfall nor snow nor winter equinox blowing
can touch this afternoon when all is still;
the heart has gathered its harvest, spring is fulfilled,
now is forever and autumn is this hill.

So, to its certainty . . .

Travel through all the latitudes of earth
the compass needle quivering on the dial
seeks its known centre, turns with every step,
sure of direction finds out magnetic north.

Hear the cool spiral curve and coral lip of shell
always murmuring with seas' unending sound
although it lies a century away
from the Pacific shore where it first fell.

So, to its certainty, the heart must turn
acknowledging no other resting place.
So from time-bounded love the word remains
singing cold echoes on the shores of space.

Winter

I

Arctic midsummer: dawns in light on light
across snow meadows where nothing grows to reap,
a shadowless world, a day that has no night,
a lidless eye that cannot close in sleep.
The long unpointed hours loiter there
holding the image of the risen sun,
brightness that shapes nothing gilds the air
from empty April till barren autumn's done.
This is an easy symbol as it stands;
add sure foreknowledge of the polar night,
eternities of darkness, shuttering hands
compelling blindness on the dazzled sight,
and all the frozen springs buried so deep
they cannot quicken into tears and weep.

II

Here's love, spent and unspent,
where shall it grow if not between your hands?
where shall it rest, if not at home with you?
where shall it wander, if it must be lost,
silence our only son, our pillow separation?
Go through the world, where people lean
out of their lives, out of a window
to speak to a stranger, to pity the unpityable,
asking 'who are you?' gentle and uncaring;
and 'whom am I?' the wanderer answers, staring.

Between our hands' close-folded fingers, time
flows like brightness streaming from a lamp.
Look in my eyes and find your mirror there,
I look in yours to find my desolation,
I look in yours and find my love unspent.

The Little Owl

Branches of ice cage in the winter here
while rain and dew are stayed in brittle light
and mirrored moons appear
silver reflections splintered into glass,
glittering like phosphorescent seas at night
whose shallows are the hoar-frost crested grass.

The silent house has eaves and sills of snow,
snow muffled windows; smoke flies above the thatch,
a width of yellow points the door below
where a shawled woman stands
calling a little owl, aching to watch
it starve beyond the kind reach of her hands.

It would not leave the angled chimney stack,
five days she watched it, clinging close and cold,
or, waking drew her curtain back
and heart sick, saw its sculptured feathers lying
closer against its breast, its wide eyes hold
points of starlight, brighter as more dying.

"Where's the lost language man could speak with bird?
How can life say to life - come, shelter here?
Will no look call, since there is no word
left to speak truce to war that man has made
on all wild creatures till his shadow's fear,
and even my hand stretched out makes you afraid?

O bird, have pity on my tenderness;
hunter, forgive trap's iron teeth and spring;
winged one, forget the caged blind lark's distress;
our lives both grow from far-shared ancestry
and meet in need for winter sheltering,
I from cold earth, you from the frozen sky."

As easily tame midnight to the hand
as tame this fugitive small bird of prey.
It lay at morning with its wings wide-fanned
and feathers ruffled by the wind to show
their warm and russet touched with silver grey
soft as the feathery snow.

Spring Evening

Out in the cold March evening on the silver branches
the blackbird's song is clear in the clear light,
and curling hyacinths in heavy bunches
crowd in the grass.
Now while the pointed buds wait for the sun
to spread their folded green;
now, when day's work is done,
while smokes of evening fires climb straight and blue
against bluer woods, I lean
on the window sill with idle hands,
watching pigeons ruffle, preen and run
while earth prepares for summer, man for night.

Noah's Ark

I

There was no presage of the coming rain
when the finished ark lay moored below the town.
On holidays the citizens came down
to see the ship, sails folded by the shrouds,
and water butts, and all the stores for grain,
and Noah watching for the thunder clouds.

A familiar landscape of wheatfields and flax
lay at the rivers edge; pasturing herds knee-deep in grass
straying, while shepherds sang. At evening
haymakers and milkmaids came home with garlands.
Days, ordinary as other summer days, would pass,
stay, linger, so diminish into night,
stay, or vanish in memory or sight
till clouds gathered, till the rain began.

Now, with the thunder, in a sudden dark
as deluge breaks across the pastoral dream
the ship wakes, each rope, each beam,
gathers her strength, becomes a unity;
life's only shelter, the protecting ark
casts her moorings to the rising sea.

II

The rain is grey, the fields are flattened brown.
Sudden rivers lace the avenues
or batter on tall doorways in the town.

Soon water will strip branch and bedroom bare,
leaves tangle with gold mirrors in the wrack,
floods lap over the last marble stair.

Now take the perfect pattern of the kind,
two of each species and no more, no more:
to outstretched hands, beseeching eyes, be blind.

Gather life's safety: here burns the only light,
here is the heart of all creation's limbs,
the only swiftness and the only flight.

Long seasons shall surround you still with rain,
moon's longer tides draw out an endless sea,
nothing promise any land again.

Hope gives a morning when the mist will break
to show a mountain-top whence waters ebb,
a flowering island, where dayspring shall wake . . .

but trust no compass, even the steady north
offers no safety now, the sky no star,
and no known harbour waits this setting forth.

III

It could be night for ever
lost between earth and sky,
mountains and islands lie foundered far beneath
where boiling whirlpools threaten 'never, never,
shall any morning break but death
on tattered sails set for eternity.'

They listen, listen, within
as lamplight rocks and sways,
each one enclosed in separate memory
or crying to time 'when will a world begin?'
Each thought a century,
while hours grope toward completed days.

It could be night for ever
where colonnades of rain
march endlessly across unending waves,
footsteps repeating 'never, never, never,'
while a wind veers and drives
white sea-crests faster round the world again.

IV

Brood, brood upon the waters, sudden peace.
Silence lies gentler than rain,
breaking clouds reveal a moon again
promise and certainty that night will cease.

Morning landfall ends captivity.
Fly freed my raven, fly, my shining dove,
from the imprisoning shelter of my love
spread wings against a rainbow sky.

Go now my children to your waiting land,
mouse, weasel, fox and spider, moth and bee,
lion, leopard, unicorn, go free,
as Adam named you, I bless each with my hand.

Here, on the future, is your anchor cast.
Go, and so multiply that air will fill with song,
jungles with strength; each go where you belong.
Only man's memory turns toward the past.

V

When all the animals had gone away
the empty ark lay beached and derelict
but sheltered humans still, by night and day.

Two daughters, murmuring, spoke of household things,
'Remember, sister, custom and custom's use,
from what tradition all our usage springs.'
'But when plants grow, will we know each by name,
for wine or balm or fibrous thread to spin?
We knew the total, but not whence it came.

We knew the pattern, each thing by cost and due,
our scope was understood; here we must discover
from what wild elements that order grew.'

Sunset flared across the desolate miles
touching bare trees, matted sedge and water,
turning cracked mud to fine golden tiles.

Then the third daughter, like a poppy, spread
her crimson veil and danced on golden feet;
and Noah blessed her beauty as he said:

'Her part is chosen, she shall sing and dance
remember legends and all names of flowers
and teach her children their inheritance.'

VI

Cold sighing waters of the flood recede,
rock slowly down to stem, to root of reed,
to silt beneath dark centuries.

Between kind elements of earth and air
water lay chained by shores, fire kept its lair
crouching on man's domestic hearth.

Man, life's image, made, marred, made again,
perpetual and ephemeral as grain,
grows to splendour, withers to despair.

While pinnioned flames strain from captivity
the heart affirms the phoenix cannot die,
but cold sense questions, 'Who shall live?

Who will escape this time to live and grieve
over lost wisdom, and with love retrieve
all loss in new beginning,

as summer leaves its seed
shut in a berry, a bossed poppy head
from one flower scattering many?'

VII

Man stole a fire from the sun
built a hearth where it should burn
to shelter him with warmth and light.
Fire his fable and his truth
blazed from heaven to crown his mind,
while, in silver censers swung,
incense rises with his praise.
But the sultry winds of hell
blow through crannies of the heart
with the fears of fires to come.
Fire in heaven, fire in hell,
both his myth, both his dread,
underfoot and overhead
clasp him in predestined flame,
unleashing all the fires of earth
to dance with shadows at his death.

VIII

Man, have pity on man.
Rain from the outraged sky
drowned the innocent earth
yet the seed did not die.
Flowering from that rebirth,
man, have pity on man
as you hold the fire in your hand
that can destroy mankind
and desolate every land.
If the power and the glory is this,
a flame that burns to the bone,
what shall be left to grow
when you and your fires have gone?
What maimed and desolate few
shall recover life's full span
from among the ashes of time?
Man, have pity on man.

IX

In Noah's ark, in safe captivity
all perfection of creation lay.
Now, chance chosen, what will you inherit,
what ghosts shall live, rise from your memory?

No bird will bring leaves from a living tree
to you, unknown, who may survive the fires
and find by moonlit craters mirages of water
among the calcined bones of history.

Shall dry bones live? Or is our language lost,
last echoes of voices singing in Gothic aisles
beneath bright ramparts of eternity
a vision faded leaving only dust?

Take all from us that our doomed hands can give.
If all we built lies fallen, still remains
the skill we leave as dower and heritage
to wake and grow again in those who live.

So save us from annihilation,
remembering our legend, take our love,
evidence of our lives, surety for your own
motive and counterpoise of all creation.

World without Man

O all ye works of the Lord,
all that imagination could compass and possess,
to whom the exhortation was to praise and bless,
to inarticulate innocence
love must resign you now with every sense.

O light and darkness,
no longer measure of toil, shelter for sleep,
alternate hemispheres of day and night, you keep
pace with the seasons for which man's names have gone.
O fire and heat, burn for yourselves alone.

Rain, rivers, waters of the firmament,
the ships of history foundered in your tide.
Our derelict gardens by the waterside
flower in a waste of roses, shoulder high,
no sight will gather into memory.

O snow and frost,
no footsteps maze the whiteness, drifting deep
in clefts and valleys, glittering on the steep
sides of the hill where living beasts still range
unremembering how the seasons change.

O winds and stars,
music and words in silence are confounded;
known and unknown flow into the unbounded
state of being, where no comprehension
gropes for meaning, calculates dimension.

O all ye works of the Lord,
freed from man's legend, his instinct for salvation,
live: for the timeless morning of creation
aged only by man's measure. He has gone.
O sun and moon, burn for yourselves alone.

The Senses

Senses are the immeasurable I,
boundaries and gateways to the state of man,
separate and inseparable
as five arches of a bridge's span:
or as a consort of stringed instruments
allowing one voice a theme's authority
to hold, not break, the others' company.

Touch

Pillowed by love,
arms fill will all content
lulled by honeysuckle airs they lie
hand within hand, the closed wings ofa dove.
Across the scuptured sheet
moonlight lies water-silver on their feet
spreading to cover them, touching at last
the dark meshed shadows of their hair,
and like a blessing lying there
while they are taken by the tides of sleep
murmuring its litany of lovers' names,
whose youth outlives their age,
whose grief lives loner thanthe eyes that weep.
Lulled by honeysuckle airs they lie
till the first sickle cockcrow tears the sky
as if the heraldic bid could see
sunrise beyond all ocean's shores.
'Children of time, your night is hurrying by.
I call the morning, for no night will stay.
This is the centuries' heartbreak you must share,
to wake to severing day.'

Taste

Give to hunger oil and gain,
dried and fragrant leaves of tea,
milk and butter, cowslip yellow,
silver fishes trawled at sea:
choose your gifts from sun and rain.

Plenty's table shall be spread
from the orchard's heavy trees,
with amber honey in the comb.
Myth of all earth's mysteries
in the harvest wine and bread.

Sight

Sight does not lodge lonely in the eye
but imagination and in memory.
A listening child beside a winter fire
learns from words to see the world
where unicorns and mermaids are
and dragons guard Hesperides:
where Minos' gold and Blondel's song
are as near as yesterday,
and comet's flight through Saxon skies
burns clearly as a Christmas star.
Vision's first spell is never lost;
its sure illumination moves
concurrent with the daily truth
that knowledge subdivides and proves
by index and cross-reference.

When the old-wives' summer comes,
September days with ripening pears
and quills of cloud across the sky,
the listener, changed to storyteller,
holds her mirror for the children's eyes
to see te landscape of the centuries.

Smell

Take the rose, in its deep smell
taste all summers you have known,
all the seas sing in one shell
and a single rose, half-blown,
gives back lost Junes whose petals fell
from a garland, from a crown.
Take the rose while echoes tell
what enchanted briars have grown
round beauty's tower and fortune's well.

Hearing

Shut into silence, cold in the stone tower,
a captive paces out long day, long night,
counting his years by the returning light,
dragging his steps to some reprieving hour.

From far, from far below the huntsman's cry
cuts like frost, and brings old winters near,
lost forest rides and the white-antlered deer,
where spiders hang their ragged tapestry.

There, in his solitude, he hears the lark
meeting the morning on her arrowing wing,
her kingdom in the sky, he is a king
whose courtiers are hunger, cold and dark.

Lost, beyond rumour's boundary, he lies
til a song's phrase shall ransom his despair,
words meet with words, echo toss the air
to crown him with a singer's victories.

Strangers, We Wear the Livery of Earth

Strangers, we wear the livery of earth,
impersonal grace given to each living thing,
shed in autumnal seasons to arise
and clothe fresh generations in the spring.
Trees that outlive men, man that outlives the birds,
flowers that live longer than the mayflies' day
touch past and present in their birth and death,
inherit all they are to give away.

Love marries us by every sense to earth,
creature in creature seeking perpetuation;
Myth is our child, in nature's image made,
to bear the burden of our adoration.
We have asked more than the natural dole
of root or wing, flower or bone's duration;
Possessed by thought our word's new boundaries
impose the heaven and hell of our creation.

Astronomers, from towering centuries,
watch constellations move in changing light;
wise in foretelling they know that life will die
and Time subside into a final night
where broken pillars of the alphabet
lie strewn across the desert's empty page,
leaving to silence and the winds of space
only the ruined fragments of man's age.

Sing, stars, that close your ranks in flame on man,
whose sight gave beauty to your radiance,
tradition knew the music of the spheres;
gather earth back into your endless dance.
Sing as you take life's ground again for death.
Man has no share in this captivity,
his spirit wakes, plumed with immortal wings,
set for his heart's assured eternity.

Wandering Pilgrimage

(1952)

Man makes delight his own

Man makes delight his own:
endless creation of his labouring days
captures for human terms all he has known.
From far-sown grain his gathered joy has grown
and, turned to sound or stone,
perpetual and unchanged for ever stays.

So, though he sleeps or dies,
his music wakes like Beauty from her night,
his words still cry his heart, for seeing eyes
his work declares how bright a landscape lies
untouched by centuries,
living beyond his perished, short delight.

The Headland

Along the coast line see the tides engrave
their contour lines in phosphorescent light
marking the rush of each incoming wave
and where the cliff foot breaks each arc of white.
Land juts above horizons of long clouds that lie
like further islands in a sea of sky.

Vision goes seaward: all the dark below
streams up the shore to storm the cliff and land
or rocks' tranquillity between an ebb and flow
leaving a line of plunder on the sand,
thin as an in-shore echo of the deep,
a wrack of dream along the edge of sleep.

Vision goes seaward: all the birds that fly
on their migrations, driven before the cold,
span in their voyage the same expanse as I,
seeing continent from continent unfold
as wave from wave rises with plume and crest,
white wings outspread and the white feathered breast.

As bird I fly to summer; and as rock I wait
endless and patient, pillar of the land,
victim of water, ceding my estate,
changing by grain and grain from stone to sand;
as woman, watch the wild birds' migrant range
and sea and land in their long interchange.

For herbs' lost magic and lost ritual charm,
made to compel the body's transformation,
leave us with only wish and thought to arm
the variable heart against time's devastation.
Grief can no longer change her tears to be
a spring that quenches thirst eternally.

Grief can no longer change her tears, no more
the hunted turn to fish or bird to share
these little silver pools along the shore
or the cool pastures of the upper air.
No roses mark where, separate, lovers lie
twining their white and red into one canopy.

Gamut of being, from life's humblest seeds,
that hold a harvest in their grain's confine,
to man's, with destiny of mighty deeds
or the traditional beauty of a line:
into predestined form the pattern flows
and grass, leviathan or prince so springs, so grows.

And subject to their bounds all creatures live
in separate kingdoms of the temporal world:
I may not turn to reed, nor as a laurel give
sweet shade from hands with all their leaves unfurled.
Yet I am woman, I am land and sea
housing this moment of eternity.

Vision goes seaward, sweeping like a wind
over blue meadows glittering to the light,
a wandering spirit, searching far to find
a summer ending to its winter flight,
a land spread wide with promise, filled with joy
dream that no truth can equal nor destroy,

where, beyond drought, beyond our famished days
the miraculous harvest stands for us to reap,
and rain has blessed it, and the sunlight stays
pent in each ear in heavy, golden sleep,
while afternoon in endless brooding peace
lies on these acres of the hearts increase.

So Moses stood alone with death upon the hill
watching the children of his care descend
to plentiful valleys, and heard their voices fill
the pass with echoes, and the echoes end.
Light died above the plains and stars lit all the air
above the inheritance he could not share.

So vision dies: from such a final height
looks down on kingdoms that it might have known,
along a coastline curving out of sight,
on the sky courses where the birds have flown,
yet is still one with bird and land and sea
housed in this moment of eternity.

The Siren

* And Uriel said to me: 'Here shall stand the angels that have lain
with women . . . and the women they seduced shall become Sirens'.

And if I sing
along these coral beaches till the caves
hold echoes murmuring
in every rise and fall of summer waves
clear as iris, curved as swallow's wing,
perfection to perfection answering,
it is of grief, a shadow of lost joy.
My silver tears fall from a ceaseless spring.

An angel, torn from heaven, defeated in the sky,
still lit by glory and still winged with flame,
in reckless beauty for the world to tame,
fell where my island basks on outspread sea,
by bastions of a city crowned with towers,
and terraced vineyards, tapestries of flowers,
down to blue valleys where my orchards lie.

Here mortal love was shelter for a day;
peace in my arms was healing for lost pride;
soon his light faded and his wings fell wide -
O wounded splendour journeying to death.
And even the memory of paradise
sank into silence, withered from deep eyes,
as like the shadowed moon he waned away.

But memory wears the blazon of his wing,
gathering me to limbs of fire and dew,
a birth of joy and grief wherein I knew
celestial language, voice of wind and star.
By light transfigured and by shadow slain
these are the songs of heaven I sing again,
mourning his beauty.
Mourning his beauty of my love I sing.

Singing I weep,
yet bright enchantment falls upon the sea
where the waves reap
their harvest of wrecked ships eternally,
for listening steersmen lose the course they keep,
forget the rocks and drown cold fathoms deep.
For none can share my joy or touch my grief.
I sing for ever and for ever weep.

* Enoch.
Quoted in *The White Goddess* by Robert Graves.

Magdalen

In a Pietà by Botticelli

Weep, your tears fall
upon his tearless eyes,
weep for the slain god pillowed on your knee
whose death acknowledges that he was mortal too:
lovely as love asleep he lies
and lost to you.

The others stand
separate in despair
learning the anguish of their broken hearts,
how far a journey can be made in grief,
how heavy is the sorrow that they bear
without relief.

But you have found,
holding his fallen head,
fingers may tell a tenderness unspoken.
Death, for this moment, gives him to your keeping:
For parting yet to come your tears are shed.
Now he lies sleeping.

Spoken to a Bronze Head

Bronze, where my curious fingers run
matching each muscle and each metal feature
with life's austerer structure of the bone,
each living plane and contour so well known,
you will endure beyond the span of nature,
be as you are now when our lives are done.

On unborn generations you will stare
with the same hollow eyes I touch and see,
look on a world in which no memories share
the living likeness of the face you wear,
keep, in unchanged serenity
all that time gave him in your guardian care.

His name is yours to keep, so will his glory be,
who are his only, his inheriting son:
and when the hand that writes so ardently
the sound of unknown sound reaches finality,
the music captured, all the work well done,
stand in his place and bravely wear his immortality.

The Bird Dream

It seems more like a memory than a dream,
the distant landscape lying blue and clear
empty of sound, no rumour, smoke or cry:
below, a gentle curve of flowing stream,
and overhead the birds sail far and near
a plumed white fleet cruising the cloudless sky.

I, with a few and shadowy strangers,
listening in silence through a summer day
hoping to hear some message or command,
knowing ourselves beset by unknown dangers
but nothing more, whether to go or stay,
unknown companions in an unknown land.

All we had left for food was country bread,
offered most gladly for the birds to share.
I went alone, knowing the gifts' full worth,
to scatter crumbs; their ritual feast outspread
I called on them as powers of the air,
I called on them speaking for the earth.

Out of the cool and furthest blue they came
turning and wheeling, circling to my feet,
their feathers shining, light as foam or lace,
white peacock birds with crests of crystal flame,
celestial creatures that bent proud heads to eat
the last food of the last of mortal race.

Now there was nothing left for hope or fear
no backward thought for what the way had been,
the last possession given without dismay,
passion, profusion, all were gathered here,
joy blazed through every sense and grew serene,
a flowing tide that bore all else away.

Then rising, rising up through veils of sleep,
through clouds and vapours, webs with points of dew,
half waking, half in dream, I grope for words
that I may have the world's-end hill to keep:
my eyes meet morning in the room I knew,
my heart still sees the flock of heavenly birds.

'Learn to love said nature, and leave all other learning'

Piers Plowman

Love, be my light, the sun to which I grow,
inform each word, be reason in each thought,
and life that burns within each seed I sow:

be the known aspect of world's time and space,
wisdom and innocence in equal rule
hemmed by the clear horizons of your grace.

Theme of life, compel and guide all less,
be word of power and summoning of sense
for all man's hope and wonder must express,

Love, in your power, let me be blessed and bless.

'All things come alike to all'

Ecclesiastes 9, 2

I am life's vessel, knowing light
knowing the separate world of sleep,
between these hemispheres I poise,
my body the one globe they keep.

All early life, assured and young,
towards my mirror I would lean,
questioning my reflected eyes
Where is love? What will it mean?

For then all promise lay ahead,
a waiting forest, where the trees
would shelter joy with flowers and shade,
romance lie pillowed on my knees.

Tall avenue and tangled thicket
fell at a word, and all was light,
wonder from wonder, I was love,
a bird at zenith of its flight.

In this clear climate I have lived,
learning the tides and paths of air,
the famines and the thirsts of sky,
the heavy weight my wings must bear.

And now I lean upon the day
as once before my mirror's glass
learning as every one has learned
how quickly, quickly years will pass.

The forest closes close again
gathering mystery into green:
thickets lie violet deep in dew
under the branches' dark serene.

Where love was waiting for my life,
power familiar and strange,
death is his waiting counterpart,
I recognise their interchange.

See, see the cradling leaves of life,
cupped hands that open to the sun,
gathered the morning for their joy
and fold and fall when day is done.

To a 'Cellist

Centaur is man and stallion, gloriously
pasturing masterless on plains of air,
a merman wears his raiment of the sea
and sphinx takes all the desert for her lair:
part human creatures, in equal part still free
in the beasts' world that half their bodies share.
Musician, hand to bow grafted in mastery,
goes like an angel where no mortal dare.

Composite being, man's intelligence
and tautened strings on wooden shell, sets free
voice beyond speech or words' close boundary
to shape a world in logic of pure sense,
to comprehend beyond experience
silence and sound in measured harmony.

A *Summer Story*

I

Here land acknowledges surrounding sea,
trees crouch in shapes appointed by the wind,
sheltering banks half hide the wandering lanes
and houses are built low with one wall blind:
the little church stands against winter rains,
stands against sun and wind in tiny majesty,

named for a half-forgotten fairy Saint
who set his mark of magic on this place.
The gate hangs broken on a rusty hinge,
and shuttered windows, locked doors show no trace
of present use: all the wild hedge plants fringe
the unmown churchyard, growing without restraint.

In lulling silence here the landsman lies
who loved a mermaid. Sheltered inshore he sleeps
whose plough and pasture ran beside the sea
along the headland where the high tide creeps
into the caves, below the fields, where she
would sail to meet him and enchant his eyes.

He lies in lulling silence, that is made
of smallest sounds, for the bee comes and goes
and bird songs lace the light days of the spring,
and falling rain pearls petals of the rose;
the lizards rustle and the crickets sing
while summer leaves murmur in ample shade.

Learn from the blurred incision on the stone
only of birth and death; what flowed between,
passion or comfort, is sealed here untold
though village legend says that she was seen
weeping among the rocks when his bell tolled,
and round his name have many stories grown.

An only son, working his father's farm,
wise with the beasts and gentle with the land,
he grew contented in his world of day;
he had the strength of morning in his hand
and April beauty, golden, with eyes as grey
as the spring sea lying in waveless calm.

In blossom-heavy air one happy night
he walked through woods, and, for his seeing glance
the rising moon lit every frond and leaf
and every flower shone back her radiance,
spring's perfection, sudden, heart-breaking, brief,
kindled to magic in that opal night.

Too early for the nightingale, yet he heard
a sound that wrought all senses into one,
as if the scent of flowers had found a voice
woven with shadows, as if the moon had known
the music of the stars, and did like them rejoice
and sang above the branches like a bird.

His heart was lost then, lost sky-high, sea-deep.
He called through thickets in the little wood:
no one was there to answer his wild words
where ash and cherry in their silence stood,
closed to his question, hiding all their birds
under a leafy canopy of sleep.

And all lay quiet on the empty moor;
he crossed the heather, his shadow ran beside
keeping his pace and mocking his despair
with larger gestures and its arms thrown wide.
He reached the cliff, climbed down its rocky stair
and stood alone on the cool, sandy shore.

The sea was shimmered with the moon's clear light
but as each wave rose up and curved to break
it turned to dark below a flashing mane.
'Voice', he cried, 'angel or spirit, wake
from sky or water, wake and sing again.'
His shadow too wept and implored the night.

Then curling water bore her to his side,
a tide of breakers was her retinue,
playing around her in a dancing throng,
and he, waist deep in seas, spoke as if words were new,
cried to her beauty, 'I waited my life long,
and if you had not come I must have died.'

'I am the water's self, of foam and light,
my beauty is a vision of your eyes,
my being, a chance of moonlight on the wave,
my voice, your echo of some paradise;
I am and am not: is there a man so brave
who would possess the sea and drown in night?'

'I would possess the sea if you are sea,
drown in the arms of night if they are yours.
What is possession? Is it to know? to take?
I know and give. Your sea has found its shores,
your night meets day at last and so must wake,
for love gives seeming its reality.

Before your music reached my inland sense
I walked the days in small simplicity
and there time's lesser boundaries hemmed my place,
now they are broken and my eyes can see
how small they crouched beneath the dome of space
where the stars cluster in vast brilliance.

What you have given you cannot recall:
if you are of myself, then I am whole.
If you are nothing O for me you live,
and in your being I have found a soul,
another sense: wisdom and joy you give:
yourself thus given, I am given all.'

As daylight came, as the slack water turned
from idling at the flood to full retreat
it bore her from him, carried her away
leaving him burdened with triumph and defeat:
morning lay cold on land where she'd not stay
but on her waves the dancing sunlight burned.

He walked home slowly; in each step retraced
he lived his search across the night again;
despair, then known, had flowered to living grief,
joy, then half wakened, lit his dazzled brain;
nourished by both he went in sure belief
that spring had risen in his desert waste.

And she, once disembodied voice and wrack of storm,
composite memory of a thousand days,
a figure-head carved by a sailor's hand
skimming translucent calm of summer bays,
and drowned girls' beauty, captured from the land,
gathered all these into her single form.

So each of each created a new creature
and from each other made a new world wake
out of the substance that was there before
imposing on each other what each sought to take,
a mirage or a vision without flaw
and earth wed sea against the use of nature.

II

Enchantment blows about a day, a place.
Return from far and it is always found
seeming to grow between the blades of grass
or lie like dew, unfading on the ground:
some moment, spent there once, can never pass
but leaves its blessing as enduring grace.

So was the cove in which they used to meet;
she sailed to him, in through an arching cave,
a doorway to the sea shadowy and deep
cut from living rock by living wave;
his way to her was down a path so steep
haste had taught him, and shod and winged his feet.

Lost all day long, only the visiting tide
strewing its shells along the curve of sand
or streaming seawards knew that they were there
lapped in the thymy breezes from inland.
More lost by night when all the stars appear
to light their beauty lying side by side.

Safe while their language is still touch and sigh;
safe while their sight is bounded by desire;
safe while her arms are haven to his heart;
safe still, although he knows and marks the hour;
safe in the anguish that they know apart,
and safe while summer fills the hollow sky.

Each day the sun and land delighted share
the ripening harvest, turning it green, then gold,
from gold to palest ivory, bleached and bright;
and down the hedges the calendar is told
by changing flowers, that in succession write
their coloured names, their scent upon the air.

He lived by seasons and their need, on land,
she lived in sea, a subject of the moon,
he was time's child and vassal, born to die,
she was beyond, below, above; too soon
these differences like a stormy sky
promised them winter gales and torn sea-strand.

For land must hold the farmer to his trade
call back the lover to his beasts and byres
use all his skill and steal his time away;
and life warms hands beside the homely fires
that cook the food and greet the early day
and from these busy hours full years are made.

Hopeless and brief the autumn burned away,
cold sea-storms broke their refuge in the cove
and each one's vision of the other died
towards the withering torment of lost love.
Each to the other sad, accusing, cried
'Why will you leave me and not share my way?'

Hearts break, and parting fills the world with tears,
and yet, outliving the small span of joy,
the pattern of delight, if truly set,
has power that no future can destroy
and stands beyond the terrors of regret
to shed a blessing on succeeding years.

And so he found it; life simple, richly spent,
a prospering farm inherited in youth,
a village wife with ebony black hair,
a new wing to the farm-house, facing south -
such things the cold sea-creature could not share
though her lost radiance shone on his content.

Her story was his lifetime, spent in memory,
living while he remembered their shared days
then vanishing, changed back to foam and light,
restored to elements. But still their story stays
haunting this shore and told on winter nights,
where inland, inland you can hear the sea.

Here, in his lulling peace the landsman lies
who loved a mermaid once. Cut in his stone
blurred by moss, dimmed by a century's weather
you see her outline, carved and overgrown
beside his name, remembering them together.
Sleep, landsman, sleep between the sea and skies.

The Garden of Delights

After the cliffs, the desert and despair,
footsore, thirsty, desperate and cold
the traveller finds the shadow of a wood,
through weeping trees vistas of fear unfold.
He gropes from thought to thoughts not understood.
Although this ending has been mapped and told
he stumbles on still clutching at the air.

But when the darkness parts at last he sees
beyond the leafless trees lie a deep glade
and there perpetual spring in all its joys
buds, sings and dances through the light and shade.
No lurking terrors threaten or destroy,
the air is birdsong, flowers do not fade
though golden apples shimmer on the trees.

No pause, no change within though all without,
the moment passionately dreamed through years
lies at my feet, a path through summer grass;
how shall I see it through this mist of tears?
Here my search ends, no boundary left to pass,
and having come unscathed through fires and fears
why should I stand before my joy in doubt?

How can such weary arms as these embrace,
or faithful hands that tore their way through night
so scarred and bruised fold love against my breast,
or eyes that learned the shadows look on light,
or heart bewildered suddenly be at rest?
Having come so far to seek for this delight
I stand in darkness still and hide my face.

Let the last courage now inform my way
and ardent truth that showed the first steps clear
shine on the ending of this lifelong quest.
Let love and wisdom in my sight appear
as the first vision showed them, whole and blest.
Turn back, my weariness; turn back, my fear;
for single-hearted I accept the day.

Certainty

In this silence, peace enclosed,
in your arms, with heart at rest,
firelight, moonlight, midnight round us,
comforted, assuaged and blest,
quiet beyond all dreams of quiet
joy lies entranced on hand and breast.

For this plenty sheds its bounty,
touches grief now years away:
to the desperate tears of morning,
to that self, from now, I say
'all is found, and your enchanted
steps will lead you to this day.'

Far, and on what unknown landscape
like a lighthouse beam is cast
this moment's certainty and refuge
for the future as the past.
Between our hands and in their keeping
Love has found its peace at last.

Quiet, beyond all dreams of quiet
joy lies entranced on hand and breast.
Within this silence, peace enclosed,
comforted, assuaged and blest,
firelight, moonlight, midnight round us
past and future lie at rest.

The thing that hath been

it is that which shall be; and that which is done is that which shall
be done: and there is no new thing under the sun.

Ecclesiastes 1, 9.

As inland shells tell of a sea withdrawn
that now lie dry and hollow in the sun
so is this temple a shadow of man's grace
whose years are over and whose time is done;
here was his spirit's shelter and resting place,
his towers were angels, his ramparts dark and dawn.

As inland shells lie empty to the day
where once some tiny creature had its hold
and shaped a curious spiral to its need,
so nave and transept stand deserted, cold,
their builder as forgotten as his creed:
the stones endure though man has gone away.

What wonder stands for truth among the blind
until their groping hands touch certainty?
What music builds its pinnacles in air
unheard among the deaf? What heresy
dares dream that timeless firmaments should wear
only such aspects as man's senses find?

When morning first divided dark from light
it taught man's eyes to see nothing alone
but all things rooted in their history,
wattles foreshadowing high vaulted stone,
and his hands learned their gradual mastery
as he pursued vision's wide winging flight.

Shaped by the fugitive spirit on its way,
cut into screen and boss and canopy,
the gods and angels of lost faith remain
the Powers and Virtues of a Hierarchy
sheltering man, who like a chieftain slain
lies by his consort in death's stone array.

Now that their words have vanished into air,
leaving no trace of what they might have told,
silence is earth and air and wind and wave
and sight is lost beneath an eyelid's fold.
Love lies by Man upon his six-foot grave,
pride at his head and at his foot despair.

Sleep, sleep in stone my warrior Mankind,
sleep Love with folded hands against your breast,
crouch servant Pride, and humble dog, Despair;
a thousand centuries are little rest
before this alabaster wakes to share
another coil the universe unwinds.

The preacher said that what has been shall be,
nothing is ever new under the sun:
late in our fading wisdom we have found
inanimate and animate are one.
Life's wandering spirit is never to be bound
but sojourns or sleeps within mortality.

Compose yourself my body to this rest;
yield to the lonely silence of the night
whose coming burns this vision on your eyes;
yield all your senses, all that was delight;
since you were born you knew that beauty dies.
Yield, for the darkness climbs about your breast.

But let the gesture of your stony hands
tell of your love, of honour and not fear.
And let this mask, stone image of your face
cry out for evermore that life was here;
from your stone limbs be born a later race.
Against the night your towering angel stands.

In my end is my beginning

I

Propped on a broken jamb, the garden door
opens on deserts. It opened here before
on branchy orchards, cool all summer through,
coloured and scented, drenched in light and dew.

The fire and power, fury of being alive
survive my spring, dried to the very bone,
and drive me to the wilderness that lies
beyond my ruins, waiting for me alone.

Alone is more than solitary now,
horizon to horizon footmark spanned,
where self learns self, walking companionless,
a single thread across striated sand:

it is the day that withers into age;
it is the sleepless night on which I lie
a hieroglyph, bare pattern of mankind,
under the changing star-map of the sky:

it is the sense that none was here before,
no kindred creature ever breathed this air
or left a trace of life as wayside alms
or token of known hope or known despair.

Stumbling and tattered flesh will you endure?
Will you outlast the soul's eternity
to spin a maze with no deliverance
on empty earth below the empty sky?

I am the miraged desert and the restless sea,
the dumb beast, blind and quivering, drenched in fear
or burning in the hollow hand of day:
the whole of grief caged in a single tear.

Anguish of time rise up and flower in me,
wake springs from rocks and summon back delight,
blessing and healing flow from a broken hand,
where the dumb remember words, the blind learn sight.

Life, in Love's image made, defaced and marred
never obliterate, still with honour tell
man's princeliness, affirm creation's truth
speaking in words made before Babel fell.

All landmarks lost: no sandstone Memnon left
singing to sunrise: and no cities' trace
lies humped in dust with all its glory down
to make a shadow in the wilds of space.

What voice can answer here but my own voice ?
What shadow fall but mine? What can be known
beyond my knowledge? But suddenly, face to face
Love stands before me here and is my own.

Whose hands cut out these features on the rock?
Whose vision knew these leaf-veined fans as wings ?
Who saw those eyes would hold the depths of space,
those hands the source whence living water springs ?

Who came before me all this desert way,
endured such night and then outlived such day
to tear divine assurance from the stone,
this first and last, this sum of all things known ?

II

I was an echo of a far-off sound,
a thorn of shadow cast along the ground
now gathered up to stature of a god.
My empty hands touched earth, therein to find
the source of rivers, their deep springs unbind:
wings spread about me, feather and filament
alert with life and power for ascent.

Manifest love, flame fallen to aspire,
burning to consume and not destroy,
infinite meaning, crown and crest of fire,
what words interpret and yet not alloy
the absolute vision, consummated joy?

Love has no shadow: one with living light,
daybreak unfurled upon the ebbing night
and exultation blazing through the sky,
I hold eternity within my hand;
a drop of water or a grain of sand,
what more was I
who am life's self, loves self to glorify?

III

The world's end lies where journeys were begun:
by quays with iron chains looped through the sea,
and rust-red hulks whose seafaring is done
and umber nets stretched drying in the sun.

The world's end lies in this familiar place;
first outward footmark is the last footstep home,
the thread is joined, woven to leave no trace
or knot this moment as a point in space:

Up the same lane to the same garden door
where all the early world of morning lies,
rain strung on sunlight through the grassy floor
and April branches flowering evermore.

Speak now my senses, in whose light I move
from radiance to radiance through the day
where heavy trees echo the clouds above;
keep your perpetual festival of love.

O apprehended self, so long unknown
beyond the tides of growth and withering,
to such a benediction you have grown
within the temporal ramparts of the bone.

Love is man's measure and his wisdom's end:
in joy's uncertainty and known despair,
he seeks no other state for heart or mind,
no peace beyond the glories they can find.

O child of substance and the elements,
charting your journey by this wandering star,
what can you make more than the thing you are?

Taking part in Spenser's Epithalamion as a Masque

His hymn to love held in one summer day
the innocence of joy and endless hope,
tranquil security of heart to heart,
long years of promise and felicity.
Bells singing in the towers
to measure out the hours
yet to be worn away,
till to stillness, through enchanted silence,
he in her beauty lost, she in his love,
they pass together to their solitude,
dreaming, beyond our sight,
lit by stars, blessed by the tender night.

I wear her garlands, where her way was love
mine lies in music, mirror to that fire
showing ghost beauty at its zenith still,
a midsummer outlasting centuries.
I give my heart for both,
my truth to be her troth,
flame in her flame I move
among the echoes and among the dancers.
Once incarnatus' woke the wondering flesh,
and still it sings the safety of all joy
while music brings them from eternity
to live our vision of their bridal day.

The Sleepless Night

'Pretender to the day lay down your arms:
native and heir to darkness find your home,
a primitive inheritance of night,
kingdom of terror; worlds before time was made
recall you to their shade.'

Safety usurped, behind whose walls I dwell,
where senses set their limit and their rule,
how shall I leave you, O my sleeping city?
Merciless darkness summons me again;
'Lay down your arms.'
Resistance is in vain.

Along the boundary of its territory
ghosts on their humble business in the house
whisper and shuffle in the corridors:
penned in the measure of Time's hour-glass
their dead reflections pass.

All easy commerce with the light is done
Worn out and laid aside, its patterns fade,
alarms increase, grow forest-high and wild
to shade despair beside a lake of tears
and shelter preying fears.

There are no weapons for the battle here:
Horror's cold fingers lay shackles on the hands
and chain the feet, leaving no escape;
while memory with tentacles of pain
searches the secret brain.

I made this kingdom of my solitude.
With idle scrawl marked on a careless chart
I drew the outline of these seas of grief,
cast countless seeds of nightmare, carelessly,
that choke their memory.

Behind the lonely windows of the dark
in deserts bordering chaos, beyond Time,
ruler and captive, abandoned to defeat,
I wait to seize upon the earliest light
to build my walls of sight.

The Beginning

Eve woke in Eden. Bright creation lay
perfect around her, home for every sense,
eloquent in perception of the day:
she, as all living creatures sharing its innocence,
had no memory of disseverance
till Adam woke: beyond that radiance
of recognition, morning's magnificence,
she saw divergence of their mortal way.

Fable of one made two, division known
only when healing seals the wound again
as spirit cries to spirit, bone to bone,
showing their fiery evidence of pain
to prove each other self each other's own.
The tokens match and yet they match in vain.

Silence and Music

(1959)

Stonehenge

By whose desire at what command
do stones stand circle on the plain
strangers that dominate the land
worn by wind and marred by rain
though quarried once by human hand?

Gate for the summer sun to enter,
grove where moon's darkest shadows fall
palisading edge and centre
when snow and silence cover all
desolate at night in winter.

Sand quivers to a bow-drawn note
and trumpets raze a city wall,
bird song, one small distended throat
is summer's voice while centuries fall
like grass swathes at a mower's foot.

The power of music hung each star
circling in the firmament:
a memory of that strength could dare
lead stones across a continent
beguiled by an immortal air.

Set free from prisoning rocks they came
like pilgrims to a holy place,
joyful in some god's power and name
made animate by strength and grace
swift and glorious, crowned with flame.

Some singing priest with king and slave
led them on that triumphant march
where stone walked lightly on the wave
and followed hill and forest path
to stand here in a hallowed grove.

So far in time from parent hill,
and so far inland from the sea,
the utmost reach of might and skill
set them as a sanctuary
where sun fulfils their ritual.

Not one remembers, no winds sing
one word of that lost music now,
or they would break their holy ring
and in a ghost procession go
after its echo following.

Joshua Trees in the Desert

This is no forest: no word for wood or grove,
all that we know as tree is here denied,
none of our words can fit, nor the winds move
this race of beings half whose life has died.

Somewhere, shallow under desert dust
they may have roots, gnarled and twisting trails
that grope for damp, water for which they lust
comes to them rarely, furiously, then fails.

So they stand still with arms and hands upraised
attitudes frantic of anguish and despair,
two arms or six, the gestures are all phrased
and almost scream the bitter thirst they share.

Some have a broken neck and hanging head,
some bow themselves abandoned, to entreat,
some lie sprawled and black, humanly dead,
and all of them are withered by the heat.

If there was one, but one, that could be seen
still standing proudly or with dancing grace,
one who wore plume or frond of green
then there would be a hope for the whole race:

hope for a spring; but spring does not come here,
these, born from prehistoric jungle seed
have waited generations in their fear,
have thirsted centuries in famished greed.

Fire could make men look like this nightmare host,
their bodies' language, mime of agony,
is likeness of mankind with all joy lost
yet life enough to suffer and not die.

Corneal Graft

At death I gave away my eyes,
translated by a surgeon's knife,
light for eyeballs dark since birth;
is it my sight revisits earth,
taking another span of life
until my heir, successor, dies?

A separate film to grow afresh,
insensate iris all I gave;
yet, if my living love should chance
to see them in a stranger's glance
should I not rise from past and grave
usurp that stranger's life and flesh?

My eye would hold and lock his sight
my bearer dumb before him stand
as grafted nerves spoke to his heart;
using live roots, my flowers would start,
spring up and cover all the land
with petals bred from weeping night.

Will one who wears my eyes in sleep
see my dreams, or do they fade?
My legacy, my jewels, hold
no trace of silver clasp or gold
no chain or locket Time once made
sapphire and emerald light to keep.

I died and gave my eyes away;
I needed none, for my dark night
is lighted by another fire;
a torchbearer that will not tire
my heart burns in celestial light,
my eyes are surety for this day.

All Souls' Day

This is the day for ghosts: from dawn they crowd
and through our homes their human memories tread;
the present is busy in time and unaware
of all that silver thronging in the air,
deaf to the words still trembling to be said,
words that must perish, take no shape aloud.

They wait for us to summon, ours the choice
to heal, complete and make peace with the shade
longed for in early, unfamiliar grief:
they seek us now for quittance or relief,
they come to us, while heedless or afraid
we will not call them to us and rejoice.

Absence was presence felt when grief was fresh,
now we have power to live without our dead
and being safe refuse to give release,
unloose their fetters with a word of peace
withheld sometime by fireside, table, bed,
nor dream that spirits wear the scars of flesh.

A last leaf falls down past the moon's face,
the rags of memory flutter in the wind
old, dusty banners in the architrave:
awake in gardens, the cocks of morning crow,
earth gathers back her ghosts. Each living mind
leaps towards morning's light and well-known place.

And this is failure and victory in one.
We have held silence, not a voice has spoken
across the chasm, having no love to spare.
Ghosts, being jealous of our mortal air,
we built that paradise where you have woken
under another moon, another sun.

Spells laid in winter

She

The window lies like ice between two nights,
the indoor night of echoes in the heart,
the outdoor night of moonless stillness, cold,
cold grass, cold silence; and all fold
the whole world in this summary of sights
that lie beyond glass boundaries apart.

I stand indoors and burn and shake and burn,
the unconsumed, the tree caught in a flame
whose winter stems, taught by this sudden heat,
force out the buds, so snow and petals meet
in white and white before the flowers turn
to fruitless ashes, fall and leave no name.

I stand indoors with fingers on the pane
drawing the cold night inwards through my eyes
till all the landscape freezes round a thought;
a net, a snare, a cage of hours has caught
my fiery frenzy that blazes up and dies
while moonrise radiance and the frost remain.

Cold is a spell of peace, a night of rest
breaking the torment of the burning mind:
this is the longed-for winter of the earth,
barrenness more absolute than birth,
an age of ice she lays against her breast
that growth and movement into stillness bind.

Rest is this lapse of pain: it will endure
as short a time as moonlight, it will wane,
be lost for ever. On a snowy bridge I stand
above a chasm: now at my command
shut in a zircon, a pale jewel's flaw
a wall of ice around a depth of pain.

See, from this hour of peace I will cry out
summon those messengers that strength can call.
One hand is fire, the other ice, they lie
upon the window pane, against the sky,
my power grasps the poles, untouched by doubt
I could command the stars and make them fall.

"All the winds that rise and blow
across the earth, across the sea,
winds that men have named and know,
and the faintest stirring breeze
on winter nights when rivers freeze,
give me ease.

By the flames upon the hearth,
by the fires that follow war,
by the blazing comet's path
his steps I draw,
to me, I draw.

Water of life where I would drink
waters of death where all must go
unquiet seas the edge and brink
of earth and parting ebb and flow,
teach and show.

Let every air
Let every place
Let fire and water
my image wear.
In every thought
and dream and sound
in word and echo
let me be found."

He

"I see with every beast's uncoloured sight
men have gone home, men live inside the days
then sleep in shuttered houses till the dawn.
Into this other world my life is drawn
this land of monochrome, of dark and silver greys,
shadows and colourless substances of night.

Each tree has learned a different song to sing
its song-bird, daytime voices are asleep
now they cry out from root and branch and sap,
rock plumes of mistletoe or let the ivy wrap
their scars of branches lost for which they weep,
or stretch twigs to the wind like a wide open wing.

In the long conjuration of the wind
there's a lost language: though the words are gone
familiar phrases cry and call the heart
back to the source of dreams where memories start
and stir the ancient dust, fable and stone,
that hide the springs of time in every mind.

This is a forest where a century sleeps
marking no change on dreaming breast and brow
of the enchanted one who waits for love.
I am led here, each thicket is a grove
to let me pass where briar and nightshade grow;
but darkness shivers and her window weeps."

Echo

The charred tree fell on ash and snow,
black windows show no light within,
but bear the distant moon's device
a sable shield where flowers of ice
climb on the glass and fronds begin
to weave a forest where none may go.

Menelaus on the Beach at Pharos

You will come home, not to the home you knew
that your thought remembers, going from rose to rose
along the terraces and staying to gaze
at the vines and iris beside the lake
in the morning haze.

Forgetting the place you are in where the cold sea winds go
crying like gulls on the beach where horned sea poppies grow.

Homesick wanderer, you will come home
to a home more ancient, waiting your return:
sea frets the steps that lie green under waves
and swallows nest below lintel and eaves:
there lamps are kindled for you, they will burn
till you come, however late you come,
till the west wind's sheltering wing
folds round your sail and brings you to land.

Stretch out your hand,
murmuring lapping sea and the lamps and the welcome wait
to draw you home to rest.
You shall come home and love shall fold you in joy
and lay your heart on her breast.

The Youngest Son

Man came last: his elders, winged and armoured
fought for pasture, each against the others,
for water-holes or caves, or went away
till all the world was peopled with their play.
Then man rose up and tamed or killed his brothers

till no vast dragons lived fiercely in the forests
no more huge flight darkened the open sky,
only the working beasts, forced to his will,
or small, wild targets for the hunter's skill
were left to fringe his world and bear his mastery.

So man grew older, rich, in silk pavilions
played with flowering times and wreathed his lance
with banners for his formal wars, and found
death's face in an hour-glass was no bound
to the proud human spirit in its dance.

In sweeping dirge and splendid requiem
he called on light's celestial counterpart
to be his soul's new universe in death,
stretched his hand beyond life's little breath
and made a heaven and hell out of his heart.

Beauty his consort, pride his native state
power his object, he conquered land and sea,
tamed the elements to suit his need,
lighted the darkness, transplanted season, seed,
grew in magnificence and monarchy.

Then, grown beyond all reason, deep out of earth
he dug remembered dragons' iron bones,
fledged them with armoured flesh, mechanic growth,
rebuilding all the monsters of his youth
that once he killed with arrows and with stones.

So man has come the long way home to fear,
the little, naked, cleverer-than-the-rest
has made himself the dragon that he slew,
imagination shows him nothing new
gathering annihilation to his breast.

Jacob and the Angels

When I was young the angels came as light
descending to my sleep,
a dream for sense to keep,
an arrogant vision illuminating night.

There in the desert world of dust and stone
no pillow for my rest,
my solitude was blest,
my journey and my halting place were known.

Never again has firecrest, flame-winged truth
descended from the sky
to seek me where I lie
as then the angels filled the dream of youth.

In middle years the angels came as fear,
walking the roads I know,
bent heads, absorbed and slow,
I heard them speak because they passed so near:

but not for me those shining words were said,
star speaks to star in light,
rays tossed from flight to flight
seen by man's eyes but uninterpreted.

When I was old, one angel came alone,
dark to my mortal eyes
he came in night's disguise;
we touched to wrestle until one was thrown.

Hip flanged on hip and palm to palm we grew
closed in our emnity
while all night's stars streamed by;
lost in each other no separate world we knew.

My failing limbs withered against his pride
and thence drew strength again
to master all the pain
that numbed my hands and crawled along my side.

When daybreak cocks crowed the horizon round
morning was my tower,
in light I rose, in power,
and from my angel's heart blessing and love unbound.

One shadow lay on dew beneath our feet,
one look between our eyes,
voices, one voice that cries
rejoicing in both victory and defeat.

All that divided us had made us one.
I was the angel, he was I,
and earth held all winged sky
clasped in the bounty of the morning sun.

The Girl in the Wood

Rain fell: I stood at the verge of green woods,
leaving petticoats under a cherry tree,
tumble of emerald and cambric under branches,
naked, entreating spring to speak to me,

ankle deep in violets by a step,
the house has gone, its floor a primrose bed,
no roof but growing branches, no wall or window,
but a quince, unpruned and unhindered spread.

'Threshold of man where the forest enters,
gate of return, I come with empty hands,
with rain on my hair as the rain adorning your leaves,
a sister to Daphne and Syrinx stands,

younger than oak, sooner to die than beech,
sharing spring with hawthorn, cherry and rose,
suppliant I come to you trees, to question your wisdom
where in the woods the tree of knowledge grows.'

Tranced in a silence of rain and doves I stood,
ardent to learn the words and truth of spring.
The rain ended and the sun glowed towards sunset
brushed leaf and hand and every feathered wing.

Then rustling steps stirring old, fallen leaves,
there came a red fox brushing past my knee,
unafraid and kin: clear language of his golden eye
reflected all that I had wished to be.

In a Studio

(Self Portraits)

See, I was this girl, quiet, translucent, less
or was I more, being rich in future then?
painting a face upon a summer field,
painting a muslin dress,
a century of years ago, or ten,
a wish unfolding and a thought concealed.

If I used words I'd name that face 'disguise',
the skill I used suggests experience,
shaped hair and cheek and mouth and all I see
to lead towards the eyes
and there I look. That was, but is not, me
gazing on flowers with subtle innocence.

Now I confront another kind of grace
and try to capture beauty's last touch of pride,
shimmer of movement before the darkening rain
falls on this time and place:
and shall I find, ten years having passed again,
another thought than this I do not hide?

Again I paint the face I see. I give
ancestral features human, passionate sense,
truth and proportion, form, colour and light.
Rapt in power I live;
my hand moves with my thought, sure and intense;
from the canvas an unknown face appears.

Martha

If I am dumb, my hands speak to the earth;
the rain, the soil, the sun bring flowers forth
but I have set the vines and pruned the roses,
at my command hedge beyond hedge encloses
the needed herbs and all the seasons' plenty.

Instinct, not thought, fosters my care that glows
on furniture and floors, the light that flows
out into night comes from lamps I keep.
I cherish order from waking until sleep;
no life can thrive without this simple bounty.

If I am loveless, a body moving to age,
yoked in service, I have a living wage
giving continuance of fire and bread:
no hearth remembers, and the hungry, fed,
do not recall the sowing, the green corn.

My hands receive the newborn and the dead
I am their welcome. I make the marriage bed,
I lay the coins on the earth-closed eyes.
I am life's minister, my toil is to be wise;
my heart is proud, my humble hands are worn.

The Hermit

(Ramon Lull)

Love turned from love: all that had been one face,
a dazzling body and lace-shadowed hair,
has driven my heart to seek another grace:
the impress of a bird's flight on the air
is not more lost than she death walks beside:
her path is set, my way is still world-wide.
O discipline of grief,
I am her exile, I her unbelief.

Love turned to love; and I must learn 'no more'
can be as rich in promise as denial.
Eyes fringed with dream look for a waking shore
unmeasured by a clock of hours, sun's dial.
The voice of solitude
is a harsh speaker of beatitude.

Earth bears all change, accepts famine or flood,
but earth has time that will outlive a heart:
grief parches man as autumn bares a wood,
and if the one who hopes, and hope, must part
accept the fallen tree,
its fruit is gathered for eternity.

I left the shaded city for bare rock.
The mountain gives me all the coasts of night,
I stand on clouds, the constellations flock
my mountain side, I pasture in their light
till sunrise fills my hands
and wakes the incense of these barren lands.

Love turned to love: the discipline of pain
has taught my body to rejoice alone:
my spirit wakes, tears are a fertile rain
to quicken flowers from the unyielding stone.
O love, be love set free
not a caged, desperate life to die with me.

The Beauchamp Tomb at Worcester Cathedral

Make me an effigy, and let it wear
my living, sleeping face. Fold my hands in prayer
and shape stone pearls to bind and net my hair;
my stateliest dress spread out to fold and flare
brocaded summer to the chantry air;
all that adorns my life shall, echoed, share
the long endurance of my beauty there.
And when my husband comes to claim his bed
in his stone likeness, I will have it said
he seeks a woman in whose sleep still shows
his other self, who was his noonday rose.
And let my head lie pillowed evermore
on a swan's wing in sable heraldry
night-feathered singer of a single song
floating on time where our drowned shadows lie.
Let my love's head rest on another wing,
my swan shall stay for his by this aisled shore
for side by side our effigies belong.
At this rejoining all the bells shall sing.
Memorial beauty, alabaster sleep
in ceremony we meet with death to keep
our marriage vows, and here we shall arise
clothed for the courts of heaven and for each other's eyes.

'The word of Lyf show unto us'

Miles Coverdale

The winter breathes its garlands on the glass
and indoors, fire tamed to its cage, the hearth
comforts the watcher who is charmed to stillness
while light flakes hide and cover grass and path
and shed a dream of blossom on the trees,
white where the may was red, the lilac dark,
making a winter night an arctic day
hiding all boundaries, blotting each footstep's mark.

The world we know is hidden under snow;
another shines upon us; eyes now learn
strange landmarks where familiar sight is stayed,
two visions of one place; each will return
in sequence to renew the seasons' circling,
as tall midsummer grass and starlit frost
seem chance and change that lightly come and go,
winter in summer, summer in winter lost.

There was a harvest goddess I have seen
belonging to the world, summer and day,
beauty serene and stately, made by man;
two thousand years under the sea she lay,
her noon, her vines, acres of barley fields
all drowned and waste, a desert of sea sand,
where seaweed fronds floated across her eyes
and hollow shells lay broken in her hand.

Water had claimed her as it claimed the town,
breaking on sleep one winter night, and she,
calm watcher over plenty, could not stay
the leaning waves nor still the shouting sea
that threw down walls and levelled all the towers,
drowned a wide plain to make another bay
where later fishermen put out to sea
and drew her up in nets and back to day.

The bronze remains; two thousand years of sea
have left unchanged the knotted hair, calm eyes
that smiled on morning in forgotten fields:
one hand upon a drooping sheaf still lies
holding their harvest, the other, lifted arm,
is raised in blessing, giving with open hand
protection to all young and growing things,
vineyards and flowers of a generous land.

When nets drew her from the sea's possession
she seemed to be love rising once again,
the unknown face that all men recognise,
search for in mortal faces and pursue in vain,
grasp, lose or find in dreams under the moon:
love in fulfilment and mystery were there.
They brought her home with garlands to the town
roses and coral crowning her sea-wet hair.

She was two thousand years under the sea,
she was a statue of man's hope of joy,
of harvest bounty and of sheltering love:
a beauty that sea-fret could not destroy,
for time is nothing to man's persisting dream,
so many harvests, so many falling snows,
births, deaths and loves, perfections made and lost
under the changeless flowering of the rose.

The poet waits through centuries for an hour
when he shall both possess and bear the earth,
triumphant draw his thought up from the deep
of chaos apprehended before birth.
The moment comes and he commands the sun,
new rivers spring between his mighty hands,
his palm and instep wear the stigmata
and he alone in naked glory stands.

How shall this vigil be endured by man
whose winter draws so quickly on to night?
What must he dare to stand in pride and power
holding the world within his eagle sight?
It is no triumph, no gay garlanding,
this is a hunt, a chase that must be run,
all forms life takes are forms he too must learn,
drown in the sea, wither in desert sun.

The voices give their warning through the night,
between the snowflakes fall I hear them cry:
'Do not presume to claim the tongues of fire,
the word of life is not for those who die,
it is ringed round by all the powers of air,
hidden by earth and guarded by the sea;
you will fall prey to talon, fang and claw
if you adventure after mastery.'

Between the snow's quiet fall and silence lies
a passage wide enough for one to dare;
open the window and let in the cold
and I'll go out into the starry air;
no certainty can name this journey's end,
I must go barefoot, without human light,
a postulant possessing only need,
to find the way that is both search and flight.

My search is known, and so the hunt is up.
I who pursue am quarry, hoped-for prey,
abandoning the articulate pain of man
for pelt, fin, feathers; I cannot hide or stay,
the hunters hold the scent and follow fast,
hot as hound's breath closing on the hare,
parting her fur against her shrinking flank,
otter after fish, hawk stooping from the air.

'Earth takes me not, I am not her beast.
Water rejects me, I am not her own.
Sky drives me down again and back to earth.
Change as I will, still my intent is known;
even the barndoor fowl, the scratching hen
clucking in dust, filling her crop with grain
finds the anonymous seed; and lowly death attained
I wait as nothing to be born again.'

Go further still, beyond this baneful chase,
stripped of time, of sense and memory
nameless, cold, even wholly without self,
barely a shadow by the archaic sea
on whose black waves darkness broods unbroken;
this is the watch and vigil I must stay,
a trance that holds before transfiguration,
the sleepless prelude to the break of day.

Raise me from here, this brink where nothing is,
stretch out creation's hand that I may rise,
clothe me with flesh again and let me go,
breathe in my nostrils and unbind my eyes.
Far sought magnificence, on breast and tongue
the fire burns: eyes see and ears can hear
the singing stars, language of lion and tree,
all glory and all sorrow I must bear.

All lost lies somewhere, waiting to be found,
the golden apples scattered on the grass
under the tree still to be harvested.
Even two thousand years of vigil pass,
the red rose flowers, twining with the white
to crown a goddess risen from the sea,
a gift for lovers who slept long apart
and meet on thresholds of eternity.

But I am mortal still, my flesh is made
of earth's known summers and the frozen night:
there are still years to claim and words to speak;
the glowing cherubim in seagull flight
unfold their wings to bound the orchard's green.
I may not stay, for where the earth fires burn
only my frost rimmed footsteps mark the snow;
the open window waits for my return.

The Dictated Theme

I

All that was home lies under those arched lids,
no quiver stirs their hemispheres of night:
nothing has changed, but the beating heart is stilled,
and no blood pulses hearing now, or sight.

All that was home is left by those cool hands,
relinquishing the morning and the day,
folding their deep tranquillity and peace,
with all remembered years, stilly away.

All that was love remains and will not go,
until the lover meets him in some night
like this one, with its early waking birds
and all forgotten flowers again, in sight.

All that was joy remains, but is unseen
beyond this moment's tears, and they are less
than sighs indrawn on the marvellous day
that wakes in distance and will come to bless.

All that was whole is like a broken ring,
one half is his, and one half still is mine,
and time will join them somewhere and remake
an image even the shadow knew divine.

II

Being widowed is the empty arms at night,
the single plate, the room where no one comes,
the memory that cannot meet a smile,
and all the simple pattern of our homes.

Being faithful is the richness of the days,
the tenderness of nights, the hopes and fears
gathered and cancelled in each other's eyes,
the deep serenity of growing years.

Being yours is to shine still, for you unseen,
to wake and turn to where your sleep was blessed,
the last goodnight, the waking morning hour,
your hand contented on my heart at rest.

III

I give you back to the free elements,
I will not hate the flame's deliverance,
the phoenix burns, and rises plumed and free.

You gave your body with the marriage ring,
you left it in my arms, and this I bring
to give you quittance of mortality.

No more in time will hand's companionship
comfort and hold me, no more lip to lip
communicate abundance or desire.

And yet the morning like a wedding day
is golden plenty, and we go away
attended by a radiance to the fire.

Be free from any tie that holds and stays,
be free to go, but all my good, my days,
are lit from your bright being and will shine.

The heart is sure and claims no other sign.

IV

In dreams and reassurances I live,
in hours and days I cannot move alone,
I go to love by stony, secret ways,
the briars fall back as if my way was known.

However far the distance to the end
I know the home and haven of my heart;
however long the spring and summer seem
that bring no new-sown harvest to my part,

I know the task will bear allotted fruit.
I know the weight my hands hold till they break,
I know the darkness as I know the light,
and all the trials my self must undertake.

No doubt unless the gates of hell are closed
and barred against my coming to their door,
and even then my way must penetrate
and stumble certain through each corridor.

Through caves where each direction offers ways
failure and promise, till I find the right,
and in the heart of death's corruption lies
disguised, despised, what must arise to light.

Follow me, follow: I can penetrate,
touch with the hand of love, and even name
disintegrate, ignoble enmity
that breaks the body with dissolution's shame.

What once was man, and loved in tender arms,
what once was joy, see, I can clothe anew
in names of love, and so recall to form,
and broken feet heal with my tears of dew:

compel the housings to be whole and brave,
compel the little to reclaim the great.
Come from this ash, this dust, to stand again
apparelled in man's beauty and man's state.

O counterpart, O love, this woman's work
is three part harmony, to be your love,
to be the full maturity of mind,
the ear of wheat, the white and visiting dove:

and last, to be the aged ministration
to close the eyes and fold the hands at rest,
the folded silence and the sculptural sheet
that lie against the stillness of your breast.

All these are done, and in another sense
I bear your body back again to give
you who are me, I who am you, to prove
our being whole, and the whole being live.

So shall the singing birds repeat the spring,
so shall the corn stand in its golden state,
so shall the waters nourish our return,
and time undo its long unopened gate.

V

Simple to speak, and now no words are needed,
thought frames a pattern more intense.
Simple to love, the heart beats on unchanged,
touch is the widowed sense.

Simple to lack, and easy to forget
the man of meaning in this new immense,
unwalled by time or hope of homecoming.
Touch is the widowed sense.

Simple to hope and in hope estrange
anguish, the true companion and defence
against the tide of day's inconsequence.
Touch is the widowed sense.

VI

If time had given us another hour,
and offered grace to part, time for farewell,
what could words have shaped from heart to heart,
what more to say that past years did not tell?
Nothing, I think, but that your head should lie
another hour pillowed on my arm,
nothing of me, all yours, you did not know
and nothing I could ask as life-long charm
to hold against the powers that divide
hand from hand, lip from lip separate,
no hour say more than all our lives had said,
so nothing stayed death's swift, commanding state.

VII

Are you a presence or a dream, I question:
are you yourself, invisible at my side?
Or have you stayed in my heart and thought so long
the impression, like a hare's form on the hillside
is deeply marked, so grasses will never grow
but bent to hold your shadow, curved and low?

Are you beside my sleep when I'm not there
but lost in night, lost beyond waking's sense?
Are you still the breath that is life in my living,
or is it memory, insistent and intense
I learned so long and now repeat again,
the echo music returning in refrain?

Are you? I ask, and who but I can tell?
I claim nothing, and do not ask you 'stay'.
Why here, when you in some far other state
are freed from dimension, as from night and day
unless you suffer too, suffer because no more
touch, sight or love are what they were before.

VIII

Look back and see, the past led to one place;
look now and see, nothing is clear or plain,
the mirage is the memory of one face,
all that has been cannot be again.

If there were tears before, why not more tears?
If there was solitude, it is not strange,
if there was hope, accept none for new years,
as there is death, I have acknowledged change.

Where there were two, one is to mourn or sing,
fire only burns till all's consumed to dust,
time is not long for elegies to bring
peace to unshared longings as it must.

Love and death are the pure themes of living,
destructable and sorrowful solitude,
the double being, locked hemispheres, unmoving
through desolation or beatitude.

IX

No longer bearing the weight and burden of time
you change, though change I cannot see,
yet by my side I sense the rising sap,
the breath of life, all truth's authority;
youth, with life's wisdom to its beauty given
perfected and made whole in this entirety.

I am the captive, I the one in chains
held by a sensual grief of time and place,
captive to memory that can with tears assail,
a travelled road that love can still retrace
to happiness and hope and long content,
not valid now, but shadows marked on space.

I know your freedom, it shall grow in me,
I know your love and mine shall match its light;
our pattern be the great birds that I saw
sweeping the sky in solitary flight,
flying for each other's far companionship
circling and meeting on the rim of sight.

Below, the earth is darkening to sleep,
the birds are burning in the upper sky,
pinioned in a morning sphere of light,
in intersecting arcs they poise and fly.
Wingless we are, but they, our heralds, keep
our meaning and our whole necessity.

Lead me for ever, as for ever past,
we came from far to be each other's own:
you go, and I still stay a summoning.
Though to the world's end each must come alone
welcome cannot be less than parting seems
nor we be separate whom love knows as one.

Silence and Music

Silence, come first: I see a sleeping swan,
wings closed and drifting where the water leads,
a winter moon, a calm where wisdom dreams,
a hand outstretched to gather hollow reeds.

The four winds in their litanies can tell
all of earth's stories as they weep and cry;
the sea names all the treasures of her tides,
and birds rejoice between the earth and sky:

voices of grief and from the heart of joy,
so near to comprehension do we stand
that wind and sea and all of winged delight
lie in the octaves of man's voice and hand

and music wakes from silence as from sleep.

Aspects

(1984)

They drink words

They drink words, lies flow on and on;
a river running in a filthy spate
quenches no thirst; corruption but infects
and poison's always recognized too late.

They eat words; a meal of rumour feeds
an appetite and crams a greedy mouth
with detritus and mould and sour decay,
they spoon them up, thinking they feed on truth.

They smell at words and like the carrion best;
they touch them too, paw with a curious hand
the blunted surface and the scurfing rust
littered through time and waste across the land.

Who would see words? Where shadow mars the form,
cut back the overgrowth to find again
the image man created, his first speech,
his cry of 'morning!' or his prayer, 'rain'.

Who would have words must marry silence first,
take thirst as discipline, hunger for food,
smell air, touch darkness, reclaim every need
before he speaks and speech is understood.

Man without Myth

He did not know his father was a tree
nor that his mother was a river's child,
that the sea rocked his cradle long ago
or that the birds came crowding from the wild
to tell him stories of their hierarchy
and teach him all the things a man should know.

He did not know his dog had ranged with stars
nor that his horse had wings he could not see,
his cat been known in temples of the sun.
All doors stand open to infinity.
He only saw a window dark with bars
and many little matters to be done.

He never saw his wife was made from flowers,
ephemeral beauty and enduring roots,
a forest murmur and a summer scent,
he only cared for the thirst-quenching fruits
and cursed her withering and autumn hours
and did not follow winter ways she went.

Nor did he know history as a road
on which he too made footprints every day.
He never used his head or heart or hand;
when comets blazed he looked the other way.
Small jealousy was something of a goad
but more than that he could not understand.

He never knew and never cared to know
more than bare necessity could show.
Once man and wonder walked life side by side:
he lost his kingdom when his magic died.

Jungles, whose growth is sudden in our sight

Jungles, whose growth is sudden in our sight,
who know that centuries must build an oak,
take only weeks to make their tenting dense
over man's empty roofs, to close and cloak
roadways and gateways. So impermanence
is demonstrated as the tendrils choke
a hovel or some old magnificence,
as silence fills the courtyards where men spoke.

If you, a wanderer, chance upon a stone
cut with a lettered language or a face
it's clue enough for knowledge to retrace
a city's plan, however overgrown.
So a name scribbled on a diary's page
brings back all youth to break the heart of age.

The Old Women

The game is long and sad each day,
the players do not know they play
sitting at gossip or at tea:
no cards, no counters, but they speak
names that are their conjuration
of once familiar hand or cheek.
They summon ghosts to stand beside
their white-lace memory of a bride,
shadow or an apparition.

All that is past has gained a gloss,
a patina that years and loss
have laid upon each history.
They do not cut or draw or toss
but bid their long soliloquies,
making new dreams of all that was.
All name perfection, none confess
to jealousy or fear or stress:
each Eve recalls her Paradise.

Each private glass reflects despair
but each curls up her pale, thin hair,
masters the change to 'I' from 'we'.
Courage the daily dress they wear
to hide their naked desolation,
descending slowly, stair by stair,
to play the long, exhausting game;
their counters are each dead man's name,
who have none, have no consolation.

The Silver Hound

Prologue

Memory is my silver hound
 stalking days that time has hidden,
searching for a past that's lost
in shadows grown as thick as grass.
Give him courage, let him pass
find the secret and forbidden,
open graves and free each ghost.
Let my seven selves be found,
quarry for my silver hound.

Lullaby

I was a cradled child
who woke to see the stars.
I thought that I could touch the sky
beyond the window bars.

I heard the song of rain,
I laughed with morning light,
I smelled the budding leaves of spring,
and knew that sleep was night.

The bough was rocked; by wind,
the tree-top cradle fell.
I knew the cold of sudden fear
but had no words to tell.

The Schoolboy

When learning came,
tall as a giant, talking of centuries,
showing me measure, weight and volume,
teaching me dimension,
bringing me languages,
laying before me all of man's achievement,
I was amazed by all these opened doors,
enchanted by the music and the stories.
But, being young, I often turned away,
calling my friends to come with me to play.

The Soldier

Look in the mirror, soldier, soldier,
What do you see?
My share of pride, of courage, of duty
and victory.

Look at the prisoners, soldier, soldier,
What do you see?
My own reflection, my wounds, my hunger,
my enemy.

Look at the shrouded, soldier, soldier,
What do you see?
My shadow, my brother, my youth, my loss,
all history.

The Lover

My love has no measure,
but the words of other lovers.
Yet my hope is boundless, garlanded and certain.
I give my promise, I give my truth,
I commit my years to you with joy.
I ask nothing - I ask everything.
Do you understand this, Beauty,
as I speak to you in the words of other lovers?

The Statesman

I have served, so now I may command,
I have listened, now is the time to speak,
I have endured, now I offer justice.
Rich, let me remember poverty.
Fortunate, let me become wise.
Steel should not forget the pain of fire
to which it owes its strength.

The Old Man

I am my own ghost now,
dreams are my company.
Saplings I set are forest trees.
Love is an echo, home is a shadow.
I sit with a rug across my knees
while small birds feed on my window ledge.

Epitaph

> What was your quarry, silver hound?
> The dead man's name means little here.
> What did you find, ranging through time,
> his joy? his power? his youth, his fear?
> Did seven selves make one man whole?

The Learning Heart

Words in their daily use grow thin and dim,
the smallest, not the utmost of their reach
- like easy shoes on a familiar road -
used without thought to answer thoughtless speech,
until a meaning burns into a life,
gives grief its weight, before, a thing unknown,
or joy, all radiance, shines as it is named
because its meaning is at last one's own.

Then, as inheritors, we see the gold,
sharp impress of an image as when new,
not blurred or dulled by all time's pastime-talk
but clear as the idea from which it grew.
So never after, on a printed page
or on a stranger's lips, will word be sound
without experience testing it again
against the essence recognized and found.

Old Letters, Old Poems

Three ageing poets loved me when I was young,
they gave me verses, they gave me stories,
they praised my work, they said I was beautiful.
They spoke with knowledge of the craft they knew,
they laid their hopes on me as if they were garlands
and each one said 'If I was young again,
if I was young again I'd be your lover.'
I kissed them lightly, taking all this for kindness,
seeing myself as an echo of their lost hopes,
I took their last loves, their last poems,
being in love myself I thought of them as friends.
But now, being old as they were then, I know
they were in love as desperately as I
and all those poems were true.

'Ainsi le bon temps regrettons . . .'

No, I will not tell you with whom I danced,
nor of the music we knew;
we stepped through the window and danced on the terrace
onto the grass and danced by the water,
the music followed us.
But long ago the grass was scythed
and with it our shadows
that danced till morning.

I will not tell you what the poets said.
I tore up their letters when they died:
no one keeps laurel leaves for long -
they get too dusty.

Nor can I tell you of love
that was my landscape,
you would translate it and see another place.

I can only say I danced,
I kept letters and re-read them,
I was loved, I loved.
You can only think it strange
seeing me now.

Autobiography

I called them eagles, so they were all eagles
floating above a gulf of olive trees,
Parnassus skies and springs and prophecies
with falling stars and dancers in the night.

I thought of islands, so there were three islands,
each one in morning seas superb and calm,
a sycamore, a carob and a palm
against the firefly clustered Pleiades.

I knew it truth, so it became all truth,
my measure stood because I knew no other:
my only truth is that we stand together
even surrounded or when separate.

I name it solitude, so it is solitude
because no other truth can touch the years
that lie like islands till the sun appears
to shape their shores or show their boundaries.

I called it love, a name that has no proof,
so it was love, created and arising,
a bird of fire, feather from flame devising
in light that burns on all the world I know.

The Field of the Cloth of Gold

Night was pavilion for our meeting,
our ceremonial, witnessed by the stars,
acknowledging each other's lives as kingdoms.
We made no treaty, only brought our gifts.
With boundaries still unchanged, as they were mapped
before we came as princes to our pleasure,
we razed the walls that once marked our division
and planted corn and vines in celebration.

Latin between Lovers

In stately, formal language you express
timeless tenderness.
You call on older words than those we used
before our thoughts, like our locked hands, were fused.
You summoned history to witness and to bless
all we can give, all we may not possess.

Thaisa and Pericles

Solitude was remembering and forgetting
seas beat through silences and dedication
while years, like waves, drowned her desolation
deeper than she had thought a hope could drown
under each disciplined and ordered day
till she was calm and cold and unregretting.
Joy was a country that she had once known
and love a city centuries away.

When time's long mercy brought him to the land
where she had lived, and learned to live alone,
they reached across the separately known
and in the orbit of each other's sight
found resurrection neither had believed.
Their recognition, proved by lip and hand,
relived their morning in their evening light
in the astonishment of joy achieved.

This is the passionate ending to the play,
the sea-ringed story of a king and queen,
a death supposed, with all that death must mean
endured, but cancelled as they meet at last.
Will they now see each other as they are
or only as they were that storm-drowned day?
Will joy reclaimed be equal to joy past
or will lost grief be their most vivid star?

Words newly paired

When words are newly paired
their own becoming astonishes, enlightens.

Immediate present, in painted exploration,
endures, interprets and transfigures time.

Usual speech, unnoticed landscape, wear their strangeness
then blur again.

Familiar disregard comes easily.
Remember the disguises of your loves.

Swan and Dove

Mate with a god, whatever his disguise,
insistent swan or cool, descending dove.
Why do immortals choose a dress of lies
to cloak desire for girls desiring love?
For each, one meeting in a lifetimes days
made cross-bred scions of earth and paradise,
a doomed inheritance we recognize,
a daughter's beauty, dazzling human eyes,
a burdened son, born to be more than wise.
But Leda? Mary? What charmed memory stays
to last through life's despairs, through mortal's praise,
or what cold hatred for both swan and dove?

The Looking-Glass

I. *Reflections*

How did I see myself,
learn my image,
in the first days of time?

I learned to recognize
my face in another's eyes.

...

How did I learn, alone
to change myself
to wear a crown, a garland?

I looked into a pool
I dipped my fingers in the water
meaning to cup my hands to drink.
I saw myself
wreathed by the reflected summer grasses.

...

At last they made a mirror out of polished bronze
where I could see my youth,
then silver mirrors for my silks and gold;
and last a looking-glass that does not blur the truth
where I, once young, will watch myself grow old.

II. *Daphne*

How should a girl, walking in a forest,
laughing with lighthearted friends,
know the footsteps following her footsteps
were a god's, pursuing?

How should a girl, singing in the sunshine,
hearing a voice echoing her song,
know it was a god's, offering to a mortal
a lover's incantation?

How should a god, seeing a girl in terror,
believe she would choose death rather than love,
see in her eyes no god but fear's cold shadow,
strange to his wooing?

How should a laurel tree, dressed in blossom,
bending its branches to a weeping god,
know that he believes she is a woman
who knows his desolation?

III. *The Flower Wife*

There was a man, a prince, who had no wife.
His friends made charms to build a girl from flowers
they wove her flesh from spring,
her voice from birdsong and her tears from dew.
She stepped, surprised, into warm human life.
But when she knelt to look into a stream
she saw herself, made from spell and dream.
How should she live beyond a summer day?
Live longer than the plants from which she grew
that winter gathers and snow hides away?.

IV. The Looking-Glass

This glass on the palace wall
is dark as water
in any stream or pool.
This glass holds images
as eyes hold them.
Mirror, or water, or glance
capture then loose each face,
but keen no trace
of those who looked, as I,
to see myself in this place
where a hundred candles' light
blazed above banquet or dance.
Do ghosts walk here at night,
do strangers who come here by chance
look, as I look, in the glass
and leave, as I leave, no trace
in the dark-as-water glass?

Nothing there

There was a pool so dark I did not know
what its depths held, what secret lay below.
I sank a shaft; it reached to rock and sand -
nothing but stone, the substance of the land;
no wreck, no treasure, no meshed roots or weeds
to weave their shadows to the sedge and reeds.
From unpolluted water, darkly clear
I stooped to draw and drink my cup of fear.

A Brink of Shadow

Here is a brink of shadow, age or hope,
but which it is I cannot recognize
though I must be my own interpreter
if there is any meaning to be found
or any message to be understood.
Here senses move alert, curious, not at ease
for nothing's blurred, nothing dulled by use,
nothing wears custom as an old disguise,
no other's words clothe this experience.
Here I must be my own interpreter.

At early morning, under a clear sky,
I, as a stranger, walk in a dell of grasses
seeing and touching, newly arrived,
solitary in a strange continent
where all is unaccustomed.
I am a stranger, one who has forgotten
all of life, needing it no more:
seeing it without memory, so without meaning,
looking, turning away
to cross a brink of shadow, hope or time.

This solitude

The solitude I own is hard as rock
made like rock of infinitesimal lives
fragments of plants, voices of distant summers
ashes that warmed a winter room at night.
This fossil trace was a bird's quill, that one a fish
and both knew movement in the elements
and both make part of a stone
which hands may carve or build into a tower.

The solitude I own is also prison;
each hour or season binds me to myself
or to my shadow that walked in freedom once.
How can I remember
which fishes leapt the shining waterfall
in woods that smelt of moss and rainy days?
Which birds were singing when I gathered fruit?
Which branches built a fire which turned to stone
as I to solitude?

No Hand in the Night

No hand in the night
gives reassurance if I wake in tears
or breaks the boundary of nightmare fears.
Solitude, with whom I live,
Silence, our other cold companion,
watch in the house, wait in my room:
when night dissolves their dark disguise
they stay inside the door to guard my day
where their long shadows lie across the years.

Clocks and Times

When the clock stops, time does not cease
though heartbeat ticks no longer stir
an empty and deserted house,
hours continue night and day
and do not stay.

When time ends, when joy breaks down
every boundary and wall,
or death makes silence stretch so long
a stillness round a living grief,
the clock goes on, the circling hands
never pause, do not acknowledge
they measure nothing as they turn.

Dialogue

'For every wound time cannot heal
reveal no sign but bear the mark,
for every night of tears, conceal
the story of the long-drawn dark.'

'For every joy and pleasure found
walk lightly, so your footsteps show
their flowery passage on bare ground,
though why flowers spring no-one must know.'

'Secret in all your thoughts, yet give
with every sense to all who need,
so take from life the strength to live,
to love in every word and deed.'

'All this is known, yet failure walks
complacent, at a shadow's pace,
listening where every gossip talks,
mocking at all desire for grace.'

Stage Settings

Places were where we went; we changed the places,
scenes for our play, light on us, with us fleeting,
but ever afterwards the town had secret faces,
each street that had been setting for our meeting.

I came to you through snow with snow on hair and hand,
then our dark footsteps marked a wide stone stair
unused by any other passers-by,
even wind made way for us, sheathing its knifed air.

Or shade fell on us from a new-fledged tree
shut in the garden of a city square,
blossoming backdrop for our meeting's silence
so unperceived it might not have been there.

Meetings and partings gone, the places stay
for whose encounters? Yours and mine no more;
someone will use them for another play
and speak the same words that we spoke before.

Fast bind, fast find

Each time the scar is shown the wound recedes,
the pain more blunted and the fear grown stale,
neither is conjured by a story's needs,
tissue and skin have closed and clothed to heal.
Colour of time, shock, courage, panic cease
as speech acknowledges a full release.

And pictures blur a face in all its moods,
they cannot smile to meet the living eye
nor change to answer thought or tears or words,
exact or in interpreting they lie.
For sight was matched with moment and each sense
took part to shape the seen's full consequence.

So truth is changed each time the past is told,
diminishing as years draw out in length,
a different shimmer lights the unchanging gold.
So hide the scars if you would keep pain's strength,
and never look at pictures of the dead
and never say again what's once been said.

Take my hand, dancer

Take my hand, dancer,
I take your hand.
See, the different flesh, yours dark, mine pale;
see the shapes, strong thumbs, nimble fingers,
whorls of skin patterns, no two in the world alike,
and the lines of life, the lines of fate,
under the differing flesh the matching structure of bone.

Take my hand, dancer,
like yours it has held bread and fruit,
knife and cup;
like yours it has touched earth and water.
See, there is nothing strange
in my hand, in your hand
that meet to hold us together
while the music guides our footsteps.
Why should either distrust, dance-long, life-long,
the meaning of the other
whose hands are as like the leaves of a single tree?

Trees

Consider trees as creatures of their own
- not fruit or fire or shelter for mankind -
see them in forests, orchards, or alone
with idiom of each species well defined.

All move to music of a range too deep
for us to recognise or comprehend:
their branches dance or meditate or weep
gestures that speak and phrases they intend.

Their saraband starts with light-blowing seed,
a winged life for the ash and sycamore,
plane tree's broken orb, nut's kernel freed
or rotted fruits feeding the pip-brimmed core.

For years, for decades or for centuries
roots go searching to nourish and sustain
a season's need for leaves, and each leaf dies
yet all new summers bring new leaves again.

As roots pierce darkness under grass and ground
branches declare this music, so fulfil
beyond our scope, song that has no sound,
dance most apparent when the dancer's still.

Weep for dead trees

After night-frost spikes of grass are glassy,
an acorn cup carries no fruit inside,
three strands of berries twist black with red, with scarlet,
ivy wreaths bare tree-trunks in the wood,
rime outlines leaves layered on the ground,
downhill, mist smoothes the change from land to water.
Which are the dead, which the living trees?
Only beeches wear last year's sapless leaves
dried to metal colours by the cold.
Masked by winter, dead trees stand with living
ranked together in their tracery:
these dead, sheltered by life's companionship,
will be discovered when the spring buds open
in summer leafage, in manifold green bounty
pierced by branches
savage as the naked bones of death.

The Late Brood

There's a black garland by the blocked-in well,
dead winter leaves I thought, rain-soaked and torn,
but when I looked again it was all birds,
their arrow-pointed wings draggled and worn,
twig legs, stained beaks, but here and there
one pure feather fitted for the air
lay on the stone perfect and forlorn,
a message from decay sharper than words.

Rainbird

Because all birds and birdsongs here are strange
for songs I hear I must invest the birds.
For tunes that draw small circles in the air
tumble, cascade and use a fountain's words,
hidden in branches dangling chains of fruit,
I draw a creature that is small and crested,
hovering and curvetting in the shade,
grey as water, white and silver breasted.

Books would name it and describe the species,
but in this garden with its plumaged grasses,
laced butterflies and lizards dragon-headed
I listen as the rain draws near and passes.
This small spring of song in the trees' shadow
gives Eden back, with all things still unknown;
because I cannot name them, they are nameless
and this wild garden is the world I own.

Fort Aguarda Beach

A man, ragged as a beggar, and his bear
left the quilted shade palms spread on sand
as if it were another century
or a memory
from which they came into full, noonday heat.

They treat each other without any trust.
He'd tied the creature to half-close its mouth
it plodded after him, roped to his hand.
Its fur, harsh, black and winter-thick,
its eyes questioning,
its body answering to rope and stick.
Bound to each other's fear
they are each other's livelihood.

Beach idlers under tasselled canopies
laugh to see the creature stand
begging for their laughter.

Being estranged from beggary's endurance
I cannot speak a word either will understand,
knowing no common language but a coin.

Devised by love

Devised by love when language is strange speech
creatures invent caresses for a human,
their claws drawn in or heads bowed to a hand
asking for touch to meet their own devotion.
Even a bird, imprisoned in a cage,
will take a finger boldly in its beak
to gentle it, forgiving captivity.

When wilder creatures, disregarding fear,
accept us, as they do another breed,
sharing the sunlight or the winter stress
we feel as honoured by indifference
as by the invention of their gentleness.
We guess at meanings left as far behind
as the shared ages of evolving life,
discarding words that cloak the human mind
we recognise their gestures by our own.

At Panjim

A mermaid fountain whitely commands the square,
those other squares have saints or conquerors,
halo or helmet to preside and bless.
I ask her story. Everyone forgets
whether she saved a vessel in distress
or brought some glorious harvest to the nets
but one last votary loves her curled, stone hair.

When he was young he fished these moon-shoaled seas.
Along this coast young men are fishermen,
women, dressed in flower and fire colours,
twist their thin dresses high above their knees,
sell the bright catch under the market trees
while the men sleep in the palm shades of home.

Now, in the shadow of the governor's palace,
he crouches on the pavement at his work.
Age has made him a landsman: for his solace
he cuts slim fishes from grey strips of horn,
precisely lines each fin and tail and eye,
then, with a file, makes each a mermaid's comb.

Galatea to Pygmalion

You made a synthesis of form and stone,
you called me woman, made my beauty whole
and capable of grace: a lingering glance
caught in stillness, a climax of a dance;
for each limb's surface postulates the bone.
You set me on a plinth of leaf and scroll
but in my eyes you ventured on a soul.

I grew from outside inwards, as you broke
chippings from marble to reveal your hope;
memory fed your eyes, eyes served your hands.
You spoke to Love, 'See where my creature stands,
let her perfections house your utmost scope.'
Who answered when your cold ambition spoke?
I do not know: I only know I woke.

I could not learn my senses by their growth
for I possess no minute nor no day.
I had no blinding, deafening, bruising hour of birth
no change from helpless limbs groping to earth
for foothold, handhold, perspective for my way.
Though I stand here as flesh and flower of youth
I have no promise, no memory, no truth.

I stand unmoving though no longer stone,
still the deliberate beauty of your dream,
achievement known before the work could start,
heartless before your too demanding heart.
Wish all undone. Wish that I still seem
remote, unbodied or broken and undone.
Wish me still vision and yourself alone.

Once upon a time

In old days, in stories that begin
'Once upon a time', nothing was strange;
Some spoke with wolves or eagles, heard trees talk
leaf against leaf, murmuring news from far
till small birds gossiped it about the sky
and though men might not understand the words
they knew it was a language.
But now our flocks and herds
are things that we have shaped and made,
they have no fighting and no mating season
but wait for us to breathe the breath of life
into their metal frames
not once but hourly, till they break.
If we listen till they rust away
we'll hear no secrets of the world from them.

The garden metaphor

The garden metaphor for Paradise entices
as leaves unfold in everlasting spring
while orchards glow with long, autumnal bounty
in shady coverts for nightingales to sing,
each shady, grassy, flowering, secret place
where lovers walk with friends in casual grace.

The garden metaphor hides facts discovered -
bird's living food, flytrap, web, sundew,
while golden creatures feed on carrion prey
or crouch to spring in copse or avenue.
Accept dead flesh and steely, watching eyes
before you name the garden Paradise.

Human

When I lived in a different time,
in a rotting house,
in poverty, ignorance and by the seasons
I did not know my ignorance,
I did not recognize misery,
it was as it was.
Then I learned new words: I saw as a shadow,
as a sickness, myself and my house.
I saw my poverty, my lack of knowledge;
being so informed I chose,
I found my way to another place.
Nothing else would have been possible
after I understood my need.
But I look back to my dark ignorance,
past generations of my changing state
and remember other things,
wondering if cockcrow and harvest
are not the images of content.

Limitations

Prologue

There's no one here:
houses behind the hill
lie in the sun and sleep.
This stony autumn cannot pasture sheep,
the flowers are seedheads for the winds to reap,
brown grass roots linger for the winter rain.
No birds are near;
waves speak, all else is still
where staring sea and sky
face each other in perpetual gaze.
So I thought, listening,
so I thought, idling in solitude and light.

But then I saw
that every curve and flaw
in rock or bent or tree
was living infinitely,
growing and dying was what I looked upon.
For beetle's track, a floating thistledown,
a ripening berry or a broken shell
were a great language, words I could not spell
nor guess at what they tell
in speech and idiom unknown to me.

Seasons and stars or shadows of a plant,
sands long smoothing in the sea's salt palm,
what calculation do these mark or own?
And what recording grains or shapes a stone
that's chosen path for hurrying, burdened ant,
or where a sunning fly in lazy calm
spreads wings that match the lichens, grown
in cutting tracery and close as flesh to bone?

And deeper still, can moss seem like a tree
to something smaller than my eyes can see
some creature lesser than my touch can find,
below the scale of sight or scope of mind?

Small

In the distortion of a summer thought
slug, aphid, ant, and all the garden creatures
grew to monsters - till each joint, eye, scale
was magnified into a dragon's features.
I, their destroyer, a patron of the roses,
diminished to an insect's minute being
saw them, great pasturing herds, all afternoon:
and ever since, instructed by this seeing,
I questioned the condition of my power.
Their dying is a pain too small to see,
their cries are pitched too high for human ears.
I bring them death so flowers shall pleasure me
and feel no claim of brotherhood for tears.

Hidden

Tulip, lily and wild rose
flower in valleys seldom seen
where the mountains and the cold
in chains of ice and rock withhold
these fragile creatures flowering.
Travellers have found this green
tapestried with sudden spring
unseen, unused: yet there unfold
tulip, lily and wild rose.

Each stem leaping from the ground
sectioned, magnified and drawn
shows precision and design
architectural in line,
gothic vaulting, tracery.

So each grass-blade in a lawn
hides structural mastery,
in each leaf-vein patterns found,
each stem leaping from the ground.

Large

A telescope sweeps through the night,
lens where my eyes grow great in sight;
miles vanish into measureless,
space makes speed seem motionless,
night's mysterious dimension
makes star and planet dark's invention
for where are they in daylight if unseen?
Where is Arcturus when the grass is green?

Unknown

From small, unseen and huge I must infer
we are enclosed by sense's limitation,
myopic eyes and the astronomer
being the limits of one variation -
dumb to singer, or, if you consider
hearing better choice for indication,
one can hear bat's cry, thinner than a whisper,
yet be deaf to crying of a nation.

So what are we who cannot measure pain?
and who are we before we come to birth?
We do not know the language of the earth
or guess how trees feel in the winter rain,
our limits fixed by heartbeat and by breath,
our boundaries are known as love and death.

Lyke Wake Dirge

Understanding death comes too late for speech,
a backward look can be the utmost given
life's values slip so simply out of reach.

So we, the watchers soon to be mourners, riven
by grief, relief, or cold from lack of sleep,
worn by endurance almost hear, see even,

presences in the room our senses keep:
outside our boundaries become aware
- even while our bodies shudder, crouch and weep -

of other traffic in a different air.
Experiencing any hour of death
we learn the rumours of another-where,

and apprehend beyond a failing breath
images of romance: the stony road,
the barren thorn trees of an endless heath,

question and answer; all the heavy load
of a life's days now to be summed and weighed
past chasms bridged by threads not footstep broad.

Bring water, flowers, and then cold linen, laid
in quiet folds upon the useless thing
while some formality of prayers are said,

though all the while our thoughts as journeying,
accompanying the stranger who has gone
and moves unseen on foot or air or wing.

We must suppose that shackles are undone,
accept escape from all time's use and wear,
jealous of knowledge, still, to us, unknown
and angry in the sorrow we must bear.

Memorial Service

His ageing widow dreams of youth,
his sons stand in their father's place,
his friends translate him to a stone,
sisters recall his childhood face,
so quickly death confuses truth.
He lies in state, corrupt, alone.

Though hopes and fears are multiplied
boredom blunts pain and stifles doubt,
words weave a dream of light and life.
His widow rises like a bride
comes down the aisle, leads the dark rout
and greets her friends as death's new wife.

The First Martyr

I

Someone must go first across the sea,
or make new words, language of voice and heart,
must build, name stars, first think eternity.

So in each life there's always some new start,
learning to touch and taste, to speak and hear,
first time to meet and then first time to part.

Later there's recognition, fear names fear,
love finds that love can be no other light,
truth once known makes its abundance clear.

When Stephen faced the stoning winter night,
his miracles, his healing, love all spent
he was the first to claim a martyr's right

to blaze the path by which all others went.

II

'Death, the presence that we do not own,
is now beside me,
a cloak of tattered pain to hide me,
torn flesh and broken bone.
My fear - almost fear I do not fear,
my shadow hand wards off a shadow stone.
The last experience, the last of need,
a shred of time, before being wholly freed
to know the light, the love is truly known
to bless deliverance, to bless the falling stone.'

III

One must go first for others to be sure
there is a road, so conquering their fear
they use his strength for patience to endure:

and more than this, the martyrdoms appear
as miracles, defeating torture, fires,
bearing more pain than human frame can bear

because the light to which their love aspires
comes sooner than the lived-out span of years
to free them from a bondage that devours.

They give forgiveness and they need no tears.

Archaeology

From pure lines of the skeleton
we cannot tell what flesh once grew,
delicate or coarse, upon the bones,
nor find a clue to its humanity;
saint and traitor must look alike at last
and love leaves no more trace than poverty.
But from a buried city's artefacts
we resurrect a race.

The Inheritor

Prologue

High sun, full noonday, where my shadow's cast,
this is my day, my strength: the years I climb
reach to achievement, if I turn back, look down.
I know myself heir to each ruined town,
harbourmaster to the wrecks of time,
rememberancer to my world for all the past.

I walk among the ruins, gaze at broken stone,
touch coin and cup, read man's silenced speech,
names of conquests, name of king and state,
trace roads through deserts to a city gate,
to the last dispossession I may reach,
the intimate sadness of some light, fragile bone.

The City

I know myself heir to each ruined town . . .

No map names this place nor marks its being.
These mounds and hollows might be nothing more
than natural rock under the wavering grass,
ripples of flowers then their falling seed.
Wild bees make honey in a hollow tree,
snakes find small sun-warmed ledges where they coil;
ants build their citadels and corridors . . .
this little world of late-come citizens
inherits here, inhabits here, survives
the long obliterate traces of mankind.

The long obliterate traces of mankind
return from darkness as we excavate,
give back to daylight street and market place.
We find the temples and the names of gods,
shrines where blessing follows sacrifice,
little votive offerings of hope
scattered, scattered, all their wishes lost,
lost as their voices singing or whispering.

The Wine Shop

Where did the orchards and the vineyards grow?

A laughing mask
above a doorway,
broken cups strew a burned clay floor,
wine jar, wine cask . . .
All these recall
a village tavern
where plane trees shade
is lightly spread
over bench and table:
a place to idle,
to drink, to talk,
for village gossip,
for evening songs . . .
remembered scent
of baking bread,
a table spread
with a woven cloth,
a plate of olives
a glass of wine.
I look again
at the broken jar,
at the laughing mask . . .
I know, I share
all that was here.

Where did the orchards and the vineyards grow?

Lost at Sea

Bright flocks of fishes move in weightless ease
where broken ships spill cargoes on the sand,
discharge their bullion, lost to history.
Who may inherit this strewn legacy,
take a Phoenician coin in his hand,
take up a broken sword where all wars cease?

Sea flowers, sea monsters guard the depths and caves;
like empty shells man's small remains lie here
rocked by the water's deeply stirring tide.
Our searching hands probe, extricate, divide,
uncover lightly what was lost in fear
then sank to rest below the restless waves.

The Mound Burial

Dear love at rest
I lay a flower by your hand,
a head of yarrow,
all I could find
in this cool land
as summer ends.
Dear love, you lie
slender as shadow
that sleeps on grass
below a winter tree.
When night's dark falls
the shadow goes
as you have gone.
Now earth must be
your coverlet.
My flower lies
beside your hand.
Remember summer,
dear love, in death,
as I, lifelong,
must remember today
when summer ended.

Avenues and Circles

Storytellers say these stones were dancers
because they pair in avenue and circle:
what was the music to which they might have danced?

Storytellers say these stones were dancers.
Masked in granite, no faces turn in greeting,
cloaked in limestone, no hands meet to touch,
if there was laughter it is hushed and hidden,
creeping grasses bind their feet to stillness
because there is no music for their dance.

Where did the rumour start - that these were dancers?
What midnight caught them in its power for harm?
Who saw the figure end, heard music close?
Who mourned their absence, searched the dancing places
but found no son or daughter, dark or fair,
only stone pillars in avenue or circle,
tall as soldiers, creatures without faces?

Storytellers say these stones were dancers;
dare they believe that stones once moved to music
that lured, or drove or charmed
these mountain splinters here to watch the moon,
to foretell all her phases, her eclipse?

The Museum

           In these tall rooms
           we walk through history.

Spears and shields once marked and stained with blood
are ranked in order, outlasting their old wars,
tortures and betrayals eased to silence;
while those who fought for long-changed boundaries
are lost beyond all courage, fear and pain.

Beauty's jewels will not be worn again,
nor household goods be used at any hearth.
Clay cups will not hold water, gold cups wine,
hunger and thirst and feasting are all ended
for those whose strewn possessions have been found
under the waves, under the haunted ground.

In these tall rooms
gods are assembled,
creators and destroyers without power.
They gaze at crowds who are not worshippers,
who know their fables, who do not come for blessing.

Patterns of life, no stranger than our own,
assembled here piece out a map of time,
landscapes inhabited by many dead
whose faces and whose voices are unknown.

In these tall rooms I find the world I have inherited.

Search

What's left, what's kept, what's undisturbed by time?
The leaves fall down, deepening last year's leaves;
thoughts wear no mark of use, no chisel's trace;
echo cannot break silence with new speech
nor a demolished house reclaim its place
nor man remake the web a spider weaves.

Take a small vertebra or rib - can bone
tell what the creature was in hide or pelt,
name cries no longer carried on the wind?
Echo lies still and dead flesh knows no pain.
Hope finds no foothold in a language spelt
by signs that offer nothing to the mind.

The change was gradual: stone by painful stone,
carried by iron when the beasts were dead,
hands hoisted upward to a bridging arch.
But stones fall down upon all history's stones.
Words shout through space, but who hears what is said?
The moon's a garden when the deserts parch.

What's left of falling leaves and falling stone?
Memory builds both tree and tower too high,
recalls a panther wreathed in dancing vines,
renames all knowledge and revives all hope.
Thought was scrawled and then obliterate signs,
its shadow writes no message to the sky.

Before whose time?

Before whose time am I alive
so shall not read their words or hear their music?

How can I lean over the great curve of years
to speak my gratitude to those who lived before me,
to say 'I hear, I hear,'
to those who taught me life?

To have lived before the lightening words
were written on the surfaces of time,
to have died before I saw the pictures
that led my sight and taught me comprehension
would not have seemed a life of famine:
but having known plenty I must wonder
how they endured and perished
before the incantations.
Some will wonder about us
seeing deeper into life than we have done
because of words, of pictures, of sounds we have not known.

History

Wise to define the sources and the safeguards,
building walls and authorising gates,
laying down roads - acknowledgement of journeys -
appointing guardians of whom we ask protection.

Too much for us to take all varied regions
into our keeping: rulers must be established,
served or disobeyed, honoured or disregarded;
unless we have them there's no choice of conduct.

So there are muses for each discipline,
there are gods commanding sacrifice,
there are virtues with their shadow sins,
all points of reference on our map of time
although the boundaries of honour change.

Earth turns and dances on a path in space
while we are certain that we stand upright.

The Prisoner

The prisoner's hand knew every stone,
the broken curve of fossil shell,
low arch and crooked flags that tell
shape and dimension of his cell
where he was captive and alone.

And soon his sight had learned to stay
brooding on lintel, bar or boss
on each green hair of dripping moss,
each shadow-change that crept across
the grille of light that was his day.

The prisoner's ear learned subtle sound,
the crack of ice, far fall of rain,
grief and fear that weep in vain,
strange voices crying through his brain
like creeping rumours of the ground.

His mouth found bread's dark taste of rye,
his lips the thirst foul waters hold.
His body ached with ceaseless cold,
corruption of dank stone and mould,
tossed in the fevers of his stye.

No freedom sets the prisoner free;
although the chains fall at his feet
and doors give back the day, the street
where voices speak and strangers meet.
Are they the shadows or is he?

He left no sign, but chains must bind
a weight of sorrow in his place.
His footsteps echo, pace by pace.
And where is he that left no trace?
Captive in dungeons of his mind.

Underground

'Once,' she said, looking at cave-concrete walls,
the hidden light that's opaque, unchanging,
'once there were birds . . .
there were seasons then, of long days and of short,
there were soft-falling rains and driving sleet,
delicate, flying snow that could turn brutal. . .'
'But the birds?' they said. She said, 'They flew,
and every species had a different flight;
some were small and brilliant in the sun,
some huge and some lived on the water.
Each species had a language or a song,
perhaps an oboe sound or clarinet
might reach the sound of that most secret language.
Old languages, written on stone or clay
could be unravelled as our scholars found,
telling how many slaves there were
what wine or oil stored within the jars
before the siege or fire in which the cities fell.
'Birdsong,' she said, 'was scrolled upon the air,
and birds,' she said, 'sang mostly in the spring
when days grew longer and leaves and flowers came,
when there was growth and change,
not the unliving and unchanging flowers you know
that cannot bud or die.'
'The birds?' they said, persistent.
'Clothed in feathers peculiar to each race,
their legs as thin as twigs, hard beaks for prey,
bright eyes . . . they lived mysterious and proud,
they crossed the seas and continents in flocks
returning year by year to sing and sing.
Some hunted in the night on gliding wings,
some of the seabirds cried like the wind at night.
In the early day,' she said, 'that was called morning
they crowded with the light into a web of singing:
waking, listening, I could half remember

the meaning of each thread of song.
It meant a memory of all springs before,
or a far country they and I had known:
I can remember it, remembering the time
when there were birds.'

Dona Nobis Pacem

You see an army going to a war
their cause acclaimed but never understood.

Hope shines as bright as banners in the morning
on lance or rifle: it is all the same,
stone, steel or fire have served destruction's scope.

Brother unknown
your hope was mirror image of my own.

By nightfall some must be maimed flesh,
health turned to pain
fear become familiar as thirst,
the cause an echo, almost lost
beyond a desert of uncounted hours.

Brother unknown
your wounds are mirror image of my own.

Beside the frontier where the murders start,
let us disarm each other, for our cause
is known, is understood
because our hope is measured by our loss.

Let us redress the wrong before it's done;
speak to me here and listen to my words,
let us absolve each other of the past.

Brother unknown
your truth is mirror image of my own.

Peace after War . . .

Here is a desert, not a promised land,
where many widows have all time to mourn,
wounds measure out its territory of pain
while derelict weapons rust away the waste
of riches that bought grief instead of grain.
Winner and loser, though each hope was born
of pride and courage, stand humanly disgraced;
victory's a bloodstain on an empty hand.

Cenotaph

Old men march to well-remembered music,
their bodies strive to match each martial tune,
old wounds ache, marking another winter.
Young soldiers think of fear, encompassed and survived.
Young women's tears fall in new solitude,
they cannot guess their loneliness is shared,
or know old women weep for loves as young as theirs,
for separate names of battles spin one shroud for grief.

Has it not all been said?

Has it not all been said and all been told,
charted and measured, criticised, re-made,
so that the chafing, scars, the strands of rope
woven, re-woven by the writer's trade
until all's threadbare, show there's no more scope
only old recognitions to unfold?

Can more be said about the state of joy?
It's known to sing in each distended vein
when hearts for long untouched, for long mere means,
lift, as if winged and liberated, sign
their scrawl of gold across the usual scenes
in lightning that discovers to destroy.

Every human says these same words over;
each city's built upon a city's fall,
all like in purpose. Each succeeding age
varies the script, yet each could speak for all
writing the names they know on history's page,
changeless names of enemy or lover.

Welcoming enemies

There's a new inclination, it is half shame,
half furtive hope, welcoming enemies
and asking for their bounty.
Earthquake, avalanche and storm and flood,
cold, with crazed fingers set in frost, to trap
tramp, climber, bird, straying indoor creatures;
all disasters known since words were made
therefore familiar; but unpredictable, therefore strange,
return and claim your victims.
You prototypes of named and unnamed gods of darkness
stretching your claws from every underworld
or bending from the whirlwind's canopy
without apparent justice, mercy, choice,
take your tythe: we offer you ourselves.
We have made arms of power and pain,
tortures and tyranny, weapons of fire;
the skill that serves us makes the death we serve
and traps us in our own intelligence.
So we must ask for all we cannot tame
the old, impartial enemies, to hurt us, hunt us
and force us back into each other's love.

What was the kingdom?

What was the kingdom?
An acre, or an island, or an age.

What was the crown?
Impossible justice married to tyranny.

What was the power?
Of life and death, no more.

What were the city walls?
All dead men's bones.

What was the river's flood?
Some said tears, some rain; but it was blood.

What was the happiness?
A single tree.

What was the city's name?
I cannot tell
for it had many names before it fell.

The Crystal Skull

All pain converges in the hidden brain,
instant communication from the eye
spreads a net to catch these mortal tears.
      Why are the innocent birds shut in small cages?

Wounds inflicted on the heart or flesh,
torture, devised to break truth or silence,
are not exalted by exalting pain,
      although stone martyrs decorate the door.

If pain's endurance is recognized redemption
it is exalted to a means of grace,
disguised as love to trespass in that kingdom
      to mock the rose by a dead wreath of thorn.

I see the reason for this crystal skull,
this shape that copies bone, but bone conceals
the brain that grew to meditate on pain,
      this crystal holds the light and nothing more.

Nocturne

The lulling absolution of the sea
accepts the swimmer into summer peace
lapping each sense in moon's refracted light,
or, in the phosphorescence of the night,
disguised in fire within the night's release
to float where stars define immensity.

This is the peace of unpossessing hands,
quiet illusion of a solitude:
for underwater, where sea-grasses move
and corals arch in formal glade and grove,
life has its kingdoms and its multitude
and other languages and other lands.

No footsteps mar the water, mark this place,
yet solitude is limited by sight
and silence by the scope of human ear.
What music moves beyond the sounds I hear,
what suns careen beyond the edge of night,
what bastions isolate the mortal race?

Rock me, dark seas of wisdom and of night;
rumours of music rise beyond your waves,
rise from your silence interlaced with stars,
recall dominion that day's knowledge bars,
an incantation that absolves and saves
flooding the dark and burning into light.

Last Poems

Autumnal

Winter will dress me soon in snow, in fear, in stillness.
I turn from that cold glass to find another crystal
retrace the way I chose to time I choose.
It lies in secret, hidden under days;
long drifts of coloured leaves or coloured hours
blow down the paths, blow down the corridors,
footsteps are heartbeat echoes of my thoughts,
my thoughts remake an image of the house.

Who sleeps there now?
Who sits waiting, waiting?
For what stranger does the light break in
announcing morning?
I have slept here and woken to new days
I have danced here, I can see
tall shadows moving in a patterned maze,
a waft of silk, a shimmering of dawn,
a long soliloquy of happiness.

Mirage, mirage . . . was this once my truth?
Vanish, vanish . . . do not form again,
outline no hope, define no tear, recall no touch,
I am beyond your reach,
no longer waiting, no longer with the dancers.

My hands were pale and smooth,
now bent and brown, now many-ringed with gold,
they loose their skills, release my hoarded joy.

Broken windows of a roofless house
let in moonlight, moonlight unmasks the shadows
where drifting snow lies heaped in silence, silence.

Odyssey

He, returned from war
from years of voyaging
and tired endurance
remembered, as he spoke of seafaring,
faces, voices, sorceries.
Neither guessed those fireside words
echo through centuries
naming all dangerous quests.

The Echo

When you were young
you would not love me.
I was your danger,
hawk to your songbird,
hound to your hare,
heron when you swam, silver as water,
changing disguises you could not lose me.

Now, when you choose me,
claiming allegiance
wrapped in your age,
flesh fails beauty,
disguise completed
pursuit defeated,
I cannot answer,
nor will I speak of love to a stranger.

Street Scene

Boys and girls have cut and dyed their hair
some half-shaved heads are crested brilliant green,
fans of scarlet, sunflower-yellow spikes
with little silver dangles in between.
Aureol their delicate, their painted features
where eyes look out from diamonds drawn in black.
Violet lips are heart shaped, or new moons.
They wear their pretty faces above rags
but clothe their legs in colours like their hair,
jewel their fingers to glitter in the sunlight.
They're humming birds and birds of paradise
flocking the streets, flights of fantastic creatures,
woodpecker laughter, shouts like crow or jay.
These are the birds that cannot fly away.

Two Saints

Beautiful girls, Chiara, loving Francis
barefoot for his sake, transmuting, if she did,
love of him to love of charity,
lies dead, old aged, for seven centuries:
while Zita, who was she? fades on an altar,
veiled and garlanded with paper roses,
silks rotting like Chiara's austere robe.
Beauties, beauties, death's decencies denied,
stay exposed to every curious eye
as blackened flesh of poor mortality.

The Moral of the Story

The cold princess, wasting on an ice-mountain
hoped a brave lover would achieve the climb,
one who would win her, save, unfreeze, limb by limb
her winter years and make her young again.
None were so strong. Her vigil was in vain.

So, if you want as much, are not content with less
than the first morning dream, than aspiration
to find a life that will engross and bless
and watch all hope wither to desperation
do not suppose intention for the best
was less than wise. Stay on your mountain crest.

Dreams

The Rose Hedge

I saw the growing hedge
a myth of rose and thorn,
one side shone with sunlit day
where we had been for ever.
When the leaves parted
for my unwilling way
you stayed shadowless, alone,
as I returned to night
holding this shred of memory
like grassblade or a flower.

The Weeping Man

The weeping man I could not comfort
might not tell his grief.
Because I held him in my arms
my sorrow found relief.

Landscape

Bastions of rock were certainly a city
unlit and distant on the cliffs of night,
clouds, defined by movement, blowing
above a plain of lesser stones and boulders
where fear should have inhabited with space and silence.
I was alone, clothed in exaltation
as if all wishes and all hopes were found
as if, in that wide darkness, I was light.

Platonic Myth

As I must go there I invent the scene.
Two springs are named. There is one cypress tree
white as moonlight. I suppose that night
has stolen colour from our darkest green
and all the flowers I might expect to see
crowding the bank must also all be white.

Frost flowers perhaps? They grew on window panes
wreathing morning in lace and fronds of ice,
rootless, scentless, winters garlanding.
Drink here? Then lose all memory that remains,
a new beginning at a heavy price,
a slate washed clean, a famine harvesting.

A meadow is named too. The other spring
is for the brave who'd take all they have found
as burden or as hope where they must go.
Is there perhaps a summer murmuring,
where mortal flowers grow on immortal ground?
This is not told, and there's no way to know.

Will thirst decide where I should dip my hand?
Will some destroying pain before I died
blur loves remembered, joy I had to leave?
I cannot know before if I command
enough of courage and enough of pride
to turn from Lethe's peace and long reprieve.

The Plane Tree in Winter

Familiar tree, a day and night companion,
sight knows so well it moves as hands might move
touching flaked bark in every sort of weather.
Leaning branches and their pendant twigs
break from the trunk, stemming from earth to air.
Stripped by autumn from a weight of leaves
it shows no common bond with vertebrates,
but, winter-bared, knows naked liberation
for light or rain or snow to decorate
beyond comparison with jewels, gold or tears.
Night draws it black against a lamplit sky,
a garden guardian, guardian of my sleep.
Summer lodged lightly in its pride of leaves;
easy as birds, in any season,
thoughts, quick as wings, have rested in its shelter.

Required reading

Princesses in those stories had no names
the title gave them beauty, jewelled cloaks,
sometimes captivity, sometimes advantages,
gifts given at birth, doweries of hope.
It all seemed simple and likely to be fact,
to ride white horses with a chosen hero
under the branches of great orchard trees,
the apples being gold, but to be eaten,
or listen to the messages birds brought,
to keep the little walnut with great care
knowing it held balldress and dancing slippers
so you, adventuring in dishonoured rags,
could dance, be recognized, set the false rival weeping
because at last the prince saw you as truth,
claimed you and gave you half his shining kingdom,
fountains and peacocks and eternal youth.

These threads have made both tapestries and cobwebs,
a moonlit park with skeletons of trees
where ghosts still walk, sighing for lost lovers.
The birds on shadow wings have crossed the seas.

Changes

I

The Cave

Stumbling by torchlight through a re-found cave
I find ancestral drawings on the rock
of fellow-owners of old plains and pastures.
Red, above broken antlers and their murdered bones,
they race or crouch or feed: familiar features
of enemies or of a pastoral flock,
recorded memories, companion creatures
known to the hunter's and the herdsman's eye
accurately traced in a dark secrecy.

When? by what torchlight? only one signature,
a single handprint marks an artist's dye,
his outlined hand - usual as yours or mine
though fortune-telling lines are blurred away -
is clear to see. The first human sign
affirming power, or, perhaps a clue
left by a father of the human line
offering all our measured time has known,
his open hand drawn ochre on the stone.

II

Dinosaurs

Roots of memory are deeply set.
It is believed that, long before man's time,
before he shaped a word or chose a name,
under ice ages, under fossil forests
dragons were buried with those ferns, those thickets
where they had pastured, mated, died,
extinct before our ancestors were born.
Remembrance holds them in a deeper knowledge
than in the burials of pre-history.

Painters remembered dragons, shaped them like dinosaurs,
stories recalled them as enemies and monsters,
dreams made them symbols for interpretation,
like and unlike those innocent beginners
feeding on grasses in an uncharted world.

These creatures of the past are summoned back,
an impress of a foot, dug from a mine,
skulls, vertebrae, even whole skeletons
are reassembled by anatomists,
confronting memories, confronting dreams,
discovering our belief in disbeliefs.

We do not know the colours that they wore,
do not recall their voices, cries or songs
more than we guess the sound of faltering words
when hunters told their children in a firelit cave
"My father's father said that there were dragons."

III

Changes

Our needed gods were summoned, from the sky,
out of the forest or the thundercloud,
to answer supplication, cure calamity.
We made them wayward, powerful and proud
forcing obedience, service, sacrifice.
We knew protection must exact a price.

The story changed, the gods made us from clay
and set us in the garden they'd devised,
left us to learn our lines and act the play;
the scenes were long and mostly ill-advised.
But we stole fire from heaven, fruit from a tree
and turned our thoughts to immortality.

IV

No *boundaries*

Our boundaries were our senses' limitation,
nothing unheard, unseen, untouched could be,
only our coloured dreams of hope
rose from each deathbed as a contradiction,
taking earth's pattern of returning spring
as an assurance.
Then lenses drew down stars into close vision,
distance, once journey's measure, now seems endless,
infinity stands for eternity.
Microscopes show, delicate, precise,
amazing patterns in all forms of life,
inheritance observed and catalogued.
No star-robed gods rule a gold paradise.
No underworld waits with its ferryman
and no redemption saves us from ourselves.
We stand as fearful in immensity
as those old ancestors at the cave's mouth,
like them desiring safety and protection.
Our offerings are love we have created,
compassion we have learned, wisdom, of which we know;
We have no shrine where we may lay such tributes.

The Voyager

I was a citizen of earth,
my time and space were easy to define,
clocks measured hours, distances were miles,
sun ruled my daylight, the moon led the tides.
She was the poets' province through all history,
lovers claimed her blessing on their secrecy.

I was her lover in another sense,
lenses showed her man-named continents.
I saw her mountains, craters and her plains.
I dreamed her landscapes, making them my own.

To gain her, claim her for my territory,
I gave my flesh to a hard discipline,
I gave my mind to science, hands to skill,
and won my way to make her conquest mine.

Flight

We were bound
as if for sacrifice.
My breath was fear,
heart beat, battering sound,
hands, cold as ice.
And still.
Last seconds spill
an earth-time past away
till heraldry of flame
burns from the ground.
This was our choice and will.

Journey

From this small cabin, my body's limitation,
I see what none have seen before today,
proving the truth of man's imagination;

cities walled by time, folded away
nature lost beyond interpretation
while colours of the many oceans stay.

Blue world, a landsman gazing from the skies
stares at the clouded globe from which he came
its mysteries closed by distance from his eyes.

There's nothing visible that I can name
though memory searches through the clouds' disguise
and love cries out for all to be the same -
the furthest landfall of known centuries.

Moonwalk

Can man touch barren soil
without supposing trees,
tread among stones and not imagine harvest,
not look for water to sustain all life?

These languages of earth have no place here.

I saw my footprint on the heavy dust,
I saw my shadow darken on the rock,
I saw horizons I had no means to reach,
I saw both hills and plains, bare to the sky.

I heard no echo sigh from any past
for death has never reached or ruled this sphere.

We came as robbers for this dust of time
to gather what lay scattered at our feet,
for purposes remote as speculation
about this desolation
that lies, unrained on, harvestless and cold.

Strange as the world before it stirred with life.

A *hope for fear*

When I return, a changeling from the sky,
burdened by homesick love, what can I bring
more than these moon rocks from our distant quest?

This cannot be a place for man to live,
the heartbreak memory of green and sea
would haunt to death those immigrants who came
avid for safety from the world they lost.

I, standing here, who wished the moon a kingdom
pursued imagination's magic strangeness,
the mirage sequences of any dream
learn my allegiance to our fading past.
What can this knowledge give to save, in time,
pelt, plumage, fin, birdsong and shadowing leaves,
from my own species' ignorant disregard?

Terror, my teacher, what I have learned I give.
Terror, command us all, teach us to live.

Excuse

Creatures had their world of sky and forest,
water kingdoms, dark to other eyes,
their disciplines of custom and of kind
learned through millenia longer than our time
as were their languages of cry and song.
We, who fight and feud with our own kind,
tamed, killed and used them, for clothing, food or work
used knife, trap, shot, to further our own needs.

No penitence was laid on us for wrong.

What bodies have been used to learn new skills
in transplant, surgery and human ills?
What creatures maimed, testing drugs and germs?
What others caged where wings cannot be spread?
What victims herded, thirsty, starved, to die
in slaughter houses where no death is kind?
In seas, polluted by our human waste
our carelessness prevails beyond our rights.

No penitence is laid on us for wrongs.

God's our excuse who made them, most, to feed
on other living creatures for their lives.
This is his blessing on our traps and knives,
our cruelties and all our heartless greed.

As *we forget*

We spawn like lemmings we despise
and waste the earth, outlaw each creature,
careless as we kill each other;
man is supposed to be man's brother.
Does justice guide our hands and eyes
as we forget and murder nature ?

Civil War

Look at your maps, a table spread
with records, boundaries changed every day
where once-good neighbours fight for once-shared land
blurred by ruins, hedged with unburied dead.
Do you, now enemies, both understand
how many deaths are a fair price to pay
for any acre? Count the yards per head
as once you counted crops of corn or hay
that fed your cattle and made your daily bread.

Biographies

How can we claim to love the dead
changeless, defenceless as they are
when such betraying words are said
whose echoes travel far?
What seemed truth and daily bread
now shows as livid scar.

How can we claim to know the dead
their secrets lost with all they knew -
a fallen tree with leaves long shed -
trifles or treasures, false or true,
a memory's grave, a sleepless bed,
debts long discharged or gifts still due ?

Gone like their voices, not a trace
of touch, of laughter, of repose.
No shadow fills their living space,
what is still hidden? No one knows.
The fragments and a portrait's face
turn to infinities of prose.

Biography as tomb painting

Pacing of hour to hour, of day to day
decades are here all crammed into a book,
pages of pictures decorate the story
show change of child to adult. While you look
young lovers smile, then wither to black silk.
While old companions have their final say
one more dead friend is filed and put away.

An Alzheimer Case

(for Tony and Ruth)

She is not she: she is as old as I,
bed-ridden mostly, sometimes dressed by others.
She remembers nothing, finds some words
and knows delight, old places all made new,
she is surprised by any flying birds,
by any cloud in any day-time sky.
She is a stranger, I to her, a stranger,
courteous and charming when I take her hand,
but not remembering any love once known
or that, once, she was my new-found-land.

So, is this love? or is this age's cheat,
or time and sickness playing a strange game,
disguise or mask, or gift won from defeat?
Changelings were young in every fairy tale.
She is as old as I and in her sight
I am a visitor she likes to meet,
telling him happy nothings, smiling, glad
of any talk she hears, not understands,
of all she sees: my half-remembered name
she speaks as question when she takes my hands.

Letter from a Stranger

If I'd stooped to the tidemark on the sand,
by winter sea, and wrack-stained, dull, there lay
a small glass bottle waiting to be found
I'd guess it held light words scribbled some summer day
- not now a cry from some wrecked castaway -
then saw my name, a crumpled paper fold
a message from the distance of the dead.
What should I do? What say?
This is the story that a stranger told,
words streamed unguided from his pen, for me,
a letter, intimate, informed and strange
with promises of long held hope and love.
I, who dared not look beyond death's change,
stare wondering at this paper in my hand
asking in doubt and hope if it can prove
time is the tide-washed shore beside my winter sea?

Sanction for love

Sanction for love was given by gods and poets
who taught the words, the necessary truth,
nourished expectation through separate days of youth
leading our journeys to the destined tryst.
We had both served these gods with some attention
in long apprenticeship to work, to love,
but not supposed, in any reasoned thought,
more than we had found upon our ways
making content the substance of our days.
Bewildered by the fortune, pain and joy
meeting bestowed, dazed by recognition,
after what centuries of separation,
dare doubt again, through any grief,
that hope outlasts all questioning disbelief?

O Western Wind . . .

An anniversary

This was our world's end day, dear love,
an end of time but not of tears,
the end of touch, the silenced word,
the first day of our separate years.
When will time end for me, dear love,
or end for both in darkest night,
or shall I find, in that unknown
your hand is mine, and mine your own?

Remembering Paradise

I can remember paradise,
exiles cannot speak of all that's lost
which silence buries, like the smothering dust
drifted on cities with unrecorded names.

For me it was a place of many flowers,
some I have recognized surviving here,
where friends, word-charmed, delight each other
with wit, with kindness and with dancing grace.
There, and then, creatures knew no fear
nor we of them, bound in a casual liking,
we played together by a gentle sea
each safe, without dependance or captivity.
Magic provision, easy for each want
gave food and drink and sheltering place for rest.
Naked or clothed, the only wearing needed
was tissued light or shadow, as we chose.
For lovers' solitudes touch was the wholest sense
that blazed, enclosed, cherished and renewed.

This is the paradise that I remember
finding its traces here, as I might find
one golden earring, lost centuries ago,
gleaming from darkness, still delicate and fine
and, without doubt, make claim that it was mine.

Time being

Time is, time was, time will be, as we play
with variants, mark time, keep time, waste time,
lose time in pastime, hightime, night time, time of day:
these measures flicker through our common speech
as if the word they name, itself, could teach
our haunted actions that there's no escape
from the short lifetime time has power to shape.

Miscellaneous

Song

Here are all summer's riches spread
by heavy hedges deep in shade.
The corn is ripe, burnt golden red,
as if the sun's own light were stayed
captive in each stalwart head.

Day's busy sounds ebb into sleep,
dew lies thick and colours fade,
but every ear its gold shall keep
until the harvest sheaves are made.
Tomorrow they will come to reap.

Echo

Echo by a ferny spring
or by houses loitering
listening since the world began
takes the careless words of man
and gives them back with other sense
clothed in mocking innocence.

Speak or whisper she will hear
and change your certain hope to fear;
take a foolish idle jest
and turn it, barbed, against your breast;
for every word she gives a wound
and only silence keeps her bound.

Be silent then, let echo rest.

Memory of destruction

Who broke the dyke and let the waters rise
must always listen while they beat and splash
by byers and sties:
see, herded in his brain, the tied beasts lash
while rope and tether hold them, as the waves begin
to run between their feet and wash
knee high, flank high, and last across their eyes.

Who broke the dyke and let the water in
to take possession of the sheltered farm
must watch it spin
white eddies through the windows, an encircling arm
holding a drowned girl masked in her drenched hair,
and see a pear tree's top still in flowering calm
above the roof that shelters sea within.

To the man who wanted a symphony to have a happy ending

Do not suppose sequence is any clue,
or that serenity following on despair
cancels its pain, for both are true.
Grief's not dethroned by joy, or dark by light
they are man's equal hemispheres of day and night.

Do not suppose succeeding years make plain
a secret code transcribing joy and grief,
interpreting man's journey. This is vain.
Either may perish, either endure through skill;
the spirit is incarnate where it will.

From a lady of seventeen to a gentleman of forty five

The echoes throng. Did you love Leda too?
And were you Astrophel at Stella's door?
Corinna – was she yours, May morning dew
pearling her hair? And was it long before
you turned to find Ianthe at your side
remembering you claimed her love with pride?

Look in my eyes. See, all your ghosts are laid,
I give them quittance as inheritor.
This is our silence. Let the echoes fade,
or will you mourn because they'll haunt no more?
Love-learned hands that hold this moment fast,
you are my first love.   I shall be your last.

Centuries taught you how to love me best
because you once loved Leda – and the rest.

For an admirer

You are my mirror: in your eyes I see
what the glass shows lit by an added grace.
Imagined beauty masks anatomy
and makes a stranger's face.

Blyth Iope, White Helen and the rest...

Campion

Beauty's a doom, a burden to be borne,
a weight of hungry glances
devour her as she passes,
demand her as she dances;
tears burn the bending grasses:
by all these crying passions she is torn.

She lives a phoenix in perpetual flame,
like gold to be possessed
or coveted or hoarded;
no thought of hers is guessed,
no hope or help afforded,
known only by her face and by her name.

Unpredictable gift, seldom and rare,
brings greed and sorrow close
and tears men's lives apart.
Yet no one dares or knows
what lies within her heart,
while every meeting is a fresh despair.

What's left for her when beauty is outworn,
and every mocking mirror
tells her clear and plain
age is a mask of terror
and all her days were vain?
Then, in each glass she dies and lies forlorn.

But she's not gone: new words and wonders rise
as any woman dressed
in youth or bright desire
some relic has possessed,
one flame of all that fire,
and shares her legend in a lover's eyes.

The face of beauty is an unlaid ghost
wandering from face to face,
staying here or there
to touch with brilliant grace.
Each woman who's her heir
reflects a gleam of what the world has lost.

Night Remembered: The Passing Bell

The story ended in remembering silence:
road, high hedges, bright and berried day,
this autumn morning changes in your thought
to winter night, lying years away.

When light was streaming through the opened doorway,
and sleepy children stepped from warm to cold,
the party ended and the carriage waiting,
the horses' nostrils steaming jets of gold.

The youngest, touched by starlight on his cheek,
by the sharp air stinging on his eyes,
woke from a drowse of sleepy pleasure
to stare alert and curious at the skies.

Orion and Charles's Wain were his companions,
the swaying lamps, hoofs beating on the road,
frost scrolled banks and spangled hedges,
high thin branches with their snowy load.

Night is strange to children, darkness a land
beyond drawn curtains, locked outside the door:
now he rode charioted among the planets
through worlds of hours he had not seen before.

A passing bell rang, mourning across fields,
the tenor bell, tolling from its tower,
crying to midnight someone's years of lifetime,
a benediction, a summoning of power.

He felt the hosts of darkness sweeping
cloud-winged across the sky,
saw spring cradled in ice-shackled branches,
and Time, like the road, flow by.

There was no longer any place of shelter,
but half heard voices, thoughts he had not known,
a night of cherubim and stars and eagles
where he must voyage alone.

Beyond the horse-hoofs beating on the road
the bell grew distant, snow fell on the land,
the sky bent round him in a whirl of feathers
and mystery lay within his open hand.

Beyond the Flames

When you submit my body to the fire
take one last look at closed but painted eyes –
allow that folly, allow some rich attire,
and say 'My lover, once, and there she lies,
she walked on earth at ease and did not tire,
she loved the morning, she let night inspire
this love that does not die, although she dies.'
But do not watch where the black smoke must rise.

You will remember me beyond the flames
that set a final silence to my voice,
and end my beauty, leaving only dust.
You will remember me because you trust
that we shall meet again and both rejoice
as we have done, speaking each other's names.

From joy to fire

He followed me, he courted me,
he would be my lover.
He brought me rings, he gave me songs,
he was the wooer.

"Take my hand, you have my heart,
my handsome lover,
all my hope and all my life
are yours for ever."

I turned to you, I danced with you,
my wayward lover.
I honoured you, I cherished you,
but summer's over.

I was young and I was proud,
my wanton lover.
Hearts are broken every day
and I will love no other.

The world is wide where you have gone,
my faithless lover,
lost is lost for evermore
and now has turned to never.

Rondel

The mirror gives assurance from the wall
that I exist and live in light and shade,
although my spirit wanders disarrayed
these separate creatures, if they meet at all,
meet in a sleepy valley night has made.
The mirror gives assurance from the wall
showing the pillows where my head is laid.

The lamplight flowering and the curtain's fall,
the chink of moonlight, and the hours stayed
between chimes, variations, hourly played.
The mirror gives assurance from the wall
that I exist and live in light and shade
although my spirit wanders disarrayed.

Old age

When with unlonging hearts we hear the wind
treading the sea with winged magnetic feet,
we'll turn to sleep, each memory stricken mind
believing that desire, in youth, was sweet.

The story ends

And it would be no comfort to our pain
to seek the heap of stones where Eros lies,
or from his limbs the heavy earth remove
that rusts his arrows, kisses his blind eyes.

For a past love

Through separate years you have become time's ghost;
years, change and happiness
have made no more, no less
the days of summer or the early frost.

The Descendant

So many lives converge in each one living:
imaginations of what million years
wake in our fears?
What past thoughts, caught in us, are giving
us our tears?
And from each one of us, what network spreading
across what future, to what distant day?
So the last man will say,
"I, blindfolded beast at the well wheel, have been treading
no chosen way,
though all seemed new that has become the past:
completed history behind me dies.
Confused, unwise,
my separate and predestined track, and from it, cast
across the desert future, blinding no human eyes,
my shadow, dark as Adam's and as vast,
unmeaning lies."

Surrey Landscape

We see the summer with familiar sight,
heat haze, like fruit bloom, lying on the trees,
the blue deep shadow where the chalk cuts white
into the tawny outline of the hill,
and willows bordering a length of stream,
the lightest wind shakes silver through their leaves,
the water where reversed they downward dream
against another sky as blue and calm.

Upon this stillness fear and grief impose
terrible vision, knowing this hill may lie
broken with wounds no time foreseen shall close,
and fire, not autumn, gild the orchard trees.
Here, as slack water idles between tides,
full summer pauses, and gives us this hour
like ripened fruit where poison hides
within a rind as lovely as a flower.

Content is a Spring

Content is not harvest gathered and stored
russet in shadow under the eaves and the beams,
to feed the needs of the people till the time for sowing
prepares the green and the flowers and the fruit and the grain
that will grow again.
Content is not harvest gathered and stored.

Content is a spring, the source of a river,
ever the same curve of the water arising,
though it flows away through lands beyond limits of sight
will fill the hands held as a cup for drinking
and answer the thirst of the heart.
Content is a spring, the source of a river.

Neighbours

She shuffles, pauses, gropes along the wall,
gathering her cobweb coat against the cold,
carrying home some scraps. She's bent, though tall,
grown ugly with lack, with Time grown old:
her shadow is distortion of humanity.
We pass each other daily; as we meet
we see our own reflections in each other's eyes;
for that instant, in each other, greet
our spectral selves: in me she sees her past,
while my fear grows, losing all she has lost.

The Julias and Simonettas
(Herrick's Julia – Botticelli's Simonetta)

Only for one was that lost face love's face
turned in radiance to meet his seeing eye.
Because this was so let no picture trace
her imperfections for posterity
so that no later moment blurs his thought
nor heaps tears unforeseen upon that day
when his pen wrote assurances and bought
her immortality with all his heart could say.

Nor search the painter's mistress' wit or worth,
see, as he saw, a moment clothed in light,
a naked Venus or a child of earth
a virgin praying in a star-filled night.
And who were they? We should not recognise
the poet's joy, the girl the painter made,
for both were visions, both idolatries
still bring with love that does not change or fade.

Collected Works

Past frontiers where all's forfeit, I still own
this one small volume, neatly leather-backed,
where all's declared: each verse is written down
and nothing left to add or to subtract.
Here's clear description, how each thought has grown
each hesitant idea become an act
tally of all that I have ever known,
all that my heart possessed and all it lacked.

Recording Angel, if an empty page
brings censure for suspected idleness,
show this production of a mortal press
and say that poets born in any age
write their own condemnation and defence
and are the judges of their evidence.

Morning

When all the birds at last set free
flew out of the unshuttered ark,
spreading their wings in ecstasy,
dawn burnished every ruff and crest
that had been dulled by the long dark
and lit each green and scarlet breast.

Along the shining river shore
flamingos stretch their necks to drink,
the ground is starred by web and claw,
white as snow-drifts on the strand
swans and seagulls crowd the brink,
while lapwings dance on air and land.

One tower, left from a drowned world
shelters an owl still half asleep:
below, with splendid tail unfurled
a peacock bows, and then advances,
before his dazzled hen he sweeps
into his formal courtship dances.

All day, all summer yet to be,
mating and nesting, song and flight,
the little cock crows from a tree,
comb and plume and ruffling feather,
he shouts for all the birds' delight,
"Tomorrow will be golden weather. . ."

"Skirts may go up to the knees again"

Evening Standard

Skirts may go up to the knee again, to the lovely knee and thigh,
and all I ask is a neat leg and a short skirt sailing by,
a pretty shoe with a high heel and a fine silk stocking
a high way on a holiday where the fair ones all are flocking.

Skirts may go up to the knee again, and they will if men decide,
for Balmain and Dior they will not be defied:
and all I ask is a windy day and full skirts flying
above fine silk and nylon mesh that all the girls are buying.

Skirts may go up to the knee again and add to the joys of life
and double the pleasure a man can take in mother, maid or wife:
and all I ask is fine yarn with lovely legs to cover,
and a dozen pairs for everyone when the Export Drive's over.

May 1944 (for John)

Do not say you cannot see
spring's white and green, being blind with tears,
nor hear the yaffle in the wood
because your grief has sealed your ears.
Look now for those who will not see
budding branch and flowering tree;
listen because they cannot hear
the early birdsong of the year.

The Feet

I hear the lamentation
of all the girls in town:
great is their desolation
for heels are coming down;
their loss of exaltation
now seems privations crown.

For tax on scent or powder
rouge, lipstick, eyeblack (or blue)
their woe was never louder
their grief was not more true,
you girls, than Venus prouder,
must wear a flat-heeled shoe.

For girls who made their beauty
from dust and stain and wood
have always held it duty
to do the best they could,
and spent their well earned booty
on face as much as food.

But pine forests of Norway
the firs owned by the Dane
are now all Hitler's storeway;
and ours, both oak and plane,
used for match, book or doorway
not for girls' heels again.

Lost is your admiration
now I to earth am near?
Your valued valuation
gone, as my faults appear?
Or in your estimation
am I your flat-heeled dear?

The room at night

The empty chairs wait beside the fire:
the night draws on in hours small and slow
the fire is quietened by the house's silence.
Waiting I listen – for what I do not know.

Perhaps for cockcrow to bring in the morning
that seems beyond imagination's reach,
or for the house to give some secret message,
or for some ghost, longing for human speech.

I should be sleeping, who trespass into night;
among the empty chairs I sit and wait:
day's traces be neglected, till the tidy morning;
I heap the wood high in the glowing grate.

Fearing to recapture the night-fears of childhood;
fearing no voice will question, night be dumb,
no step seek my presence, no stranger passing
find my vigil, and no vision come.

This night has neither wind nor moonlight,
frost holds the world in chains of iron and ice,
cold creeps through keyholes and the edge of windows
stronger than hearth or house of man's device.

Between the fire and the cold I wait,
shut, impatient, in night's patient peace
along with clock and firelight in besieging winter
until the morning cockcrow brings release.

To *celebrate* the Dressmakers

I sing the seamstress, she whose careful art
(here a gather, there a well placed dart)
does more than nature did for most of us
to bring more near th' Ideal, the Glamorous –
the vision that our hopeful eyes behold
half Fashion's dream and half the Age of Gold.
(And in a breath, a bracket, let me say
words to the careless who do not look this way,
the thoughtless shes, whose petticoats down-hang
the grubby ankled, unbrushed, unpressed gang...
how should the cleverest dressmaker be able
to help, to mould, to glorify such rabble?)
O not in vanity this song I raise:
though none deny, not I, how lovely's praise,
happy, the heart answers each tender sound
murmurs that praise, and Dress with Girl confound
in one delighted and delighting love.
In gratitude, not vanity, my pen shall move.
O Dressmakers, great is your power, and you
have wit and virtue, sometimes malice too.
I, to your qualities owe many a happy hour,
(and many a bill.) (That shall not make me sour.)
I shall rejoice! For money is well spent
that buys me elegance, pays for content
each time I see my happy swain who smiles
on me, on you, and on our mutual wiles.

The Gardener's Calendar

October

Yellow October! Leaves on dew-white grass
brighter than apple's gold or russet fruit. . .
No time to stand and stare, your gardening suit
is on for sterner work, and you, alas,
must sweep, and burn, and make the garden pass
a tidy autumn; so, you must uproot
all the dead annuals, sow the early cress,
mustard and radishes (not with an odorous foot).

For other work – those carrots you deplore
must all be pulled before the frosts begin,
and you should gather all the beetroots in,
and in some place both dark and dry them store;
plant rhubarb; and, to keep them white and pure,
cabbage and celery should be earthed up the more.

November

Remember remember
that in November
you must plant broad beans,
you must earth up the greens,
spring will mature.
And it is time
to dress the earth with lime.
All this I am sure
is right for November.

December

Sing Noel, but yet spare time
to save your treasures from frost and rime.
Think of May, and plant dwarf peas
in a sheltered spot not under trees.
Start potatoes to sprout in boxes
in warmth and light and free of shockses.

January

Think of the future,
make a resolution
to wrest from nature
gastronomic consolation.
Sow mushrooms now, and leeks,
lettuce and onion seed . . .
O may they, fertile, breed
all your cook seeks. . .
and at the seedsman's, choose
all that this year you'll use.

February

February fill dyke, and you in gumboots, going
hither and thither on your land and for the future sowing
broad beans,
   tomatoes,
     cabbage,
       lettuces,
         mustard and cress,
and anything else you can think of or have time to do.
And,
plant with hands quite tired of sowing
the other things that you can buy, half growing,
onions, and artichokes and small shallots,
(and of the latter I would put in lots).

March

Lion or Lamb? The earliest days of spring
are often cold as never winter's worst,
and, frequently, all the house pipes will burst;
and, if your winter garments of repentance fling,
you get a chill. Now to your garden bring
broad beans and early peas – second sowing,
and put in rather more than you did first –
and plant your rows of parsley straight as string.

Only like this, before the swallow dares,
can you, like daffodils in jubilation,
express in terms of earth your celebration;
and in this month there'll be no weed, no tare,
so you for once will have some time to spare
and garden fit for self congratulation.

April

April, April. . .
to hell with girlish laughter,
read what follows after,
more need for sweat and tears.

Sow and plant
leeks and cabbage and sprouts and peas
marrow, salsify, turnips and beet,
runner beans and cauliflower,
will you have a spare half hour
to add carrots to all these?
(Not ones like mandrakes if you please).
Don't say you can't
also
hoe between the rows, and dust
with derris powder, for you must.

May

Maytime of flower and song
and love and kisses!
But all of this the gardener misses
sowing and growing
salads of all kinds, spinach and still more peas,
and staking earlier crops of these,
earthing potatoes, top-dressing with manure. . .
flowers and songs are much more fun I'm sure,
O dear, O dear, what the poor gardener misses
by being too tired for love and kisses.

June

Come lyric June! But still no rest for you;
the ever-sowing hand must sow again,
kohl-rabi, spinach, of runner-beans a few,
and helped by gentle sun and summer rain
plant marrow and celery against the winter's pain,
and dig the first potatoes up again,
- that is a word that in the gardener's brain
is ever present: nothing is ever new.

Go pinch the bright top leaves from off the beans,
and nightly water all your cherished greens,
(Lord! What a sweat this gardening racket means),
but new potatoes and the first young peas
are pretty good, and everybody sees
how well you thrive on these activities.

July

Both sow and gather.
The full year pauses, and first crops brought in
are token of what honest toil can win
from soil.
But I had rather
pick crimson cherries
and currants like scarlet pearls,
and probably I speak for all the girls,
than ever toil
towards the winter's grannaries and garrets
full of beets, and celery and carrots.
Rather be still through the long afternoon
than sow, as you should soon,
colewort and endive, parsley for winter pies,
radish and onion, that gentlier in the allotment lies
than in the cook's hand, while she unwilling cries.
No! give me cherries, and I will idle here
while others plant late harvests of the year.

August

August is come: sow onions, yes, again,
spinach and coleworts, do I speak in vain?
Plant mushrooms then, and let the others go
there'll be enough by now if all do grow.
Lift your potatoes, gather in the beans,
and burn the plants, they will have no more flowers,
cut the huge artichokes, to eat they take some hours
but are the very nicest kind of greens,
and say: my summer has been good for dish and table;
I am a gardener good and capable.

September

September: tidy up the beds,
dry the heavy sunflower heads,
dry the onions you have grown,
tie them in garlands copper brown.
Clear and sweep, the summer's done,
from flower to fruit the apple's grown;
through summer's warmth your mind will turn
when green were leaves that now must burn.
But in the earth, beyond our sight
another summer sleeps its night,
and may next year be flowers and trees,
honey and sweetness, and all these
be added to the greens and roots
and all the richest of earth's fruits,
never louse nor bug nor worm
blight nor greenfly do you harm.

Index of Titles

Index of Titles

Index of First Lines

Index of First Lines

Ursula Wood (1933)

Capt. Michael Forrester Wood
(1933)

Ursula marries Michael, May 24 1933, at St. Clement Danes in London

Ursula at her marriage with Ralph Vaughan Williams, February 7 1953

Ursula and Ralph at a Royal Philharmonic concert (1957)

Ursula and Ralph study a score
(1957)

Above - Ursula and Ralph at Haddo House, Aberdeen (1957)

Opposite - Ursula and Ralph outside their home at 10 Hanover Terrace in London (1957)

Ursula with Melvyn Bragg (1984)

Ursula with Joseph Ward (1985)

Fall of Leaf

"Not always fall of leaf, nor ever spring,
no endless night, yet not eternal day."

Southwell

Chapter 1

"Won't she be pretty lonely there?" Francis asked Alice with concern.

"She thinks of it as exile, of course," Alice said pouring out her fourth cup of coffee. "But you know, as well as I do, that she's not fit to go home yet. If you can't carry a kettle - or a coffee pot – " " - or a whisky bottle" he finished the sentence for her, "you can't be alone in a flat. Fair enough - we'll have to go and visit her even more often."

"You've been very good about that."

"Well, I do find her remarkable, and when she's being bitchy she's amazingly lively with it."

"And you like some of her music - I wonder if she'll ever be able to write again - it's rotten luck breaking so many bones all at once."

They were having breakfast in the garden. It was sunny without, as yet, being a dazzling morning. The garden smelt deliciously of honeysuckle, the roses were out. Neither Francis nor Alice cared for weeding, but even the midsummer weeds were pretty, caught in a dappled light under a small maytree and rose bushes. Three steps led down to the little paved area, where they had arranged two garden seats and a square table. 'Nothing that has to be washed or re-painted' Alice had decided when they bought the house twelve years ago. It was in one of the crescents in Camden, not far from Regent's Park, and where the houses were early enough Victorian to have more of an air of belonging to the Regency than to the Victorian period of architectural self-satisfaction. Their house was small, and only two stories high, though it was, as they liked to say, blessed with a basement that was too dark to make them feel that they ought to turn it into a flat that should be let. They used it for a spare bedroom - and a boxroom - an old-fashioned luxury.

It was a Saturday morning; one of their habits had been to make Saturdays as idle as possible, to share a whole day with each other, inventing treats and excursions never, if possible, having other people involved for entertaining or being entertained. They had been married for ages, sixteen years, and had fallen into this ritual early in their lives together. It had, very occasionally, to be given up for one reason or another, today being one of the sacrifices. Their friend Stella had been in hospital after a bad fall. Francis had immediately guessed that she'd been drinking too much; Alice, who'd been summoned by neighbours in the middle of the night knew that she had - Francis had been away at the time - but it was bad luck, too, that she'd fallen over the suitcase she'd left half packed by her bedside, when she'd been woken by what she thought was a burglar trying to break down her door - a periodical nightmare in her life.

Anyway, Alice had gone with her in the ambulance, seen her in hospital, and generally taken charge, and it was she who had arranged for this convalescence. Francis asked, for the third time since they'd got up, if she wouldn't like him to come too, for the third time she'd let him off. He could see that he might as well accept. He was grateful, for though Stella was more his friend than hers, Alice was the one who was involved with her destination, a place referred to variously by its proper name, Marion House, or 'poor Henry's folly', 'Bedlam', or 'that place in Hampstead-you-know' according to the speaker. It was a popular retreat.

"Well," he said, "don't feel so worried about it, she's going to enjoy being a problem while she's there."

Alice laughed. "I know, but there are all the others to think of."

"They'll enjoy it too - a good deal of drama I expect."

He smiled at her, and thought that he'd think of some surprise for her for when she came home. They were both in their dressing gowns.

Francis's was a towelling one with a big pocket, bulging with things he might need, biro, notebook, glasses, cigarette lighter, tin of small cigars, a packet of little malt pills - the cats had their Saturday morning treat too - and other oddments. Alice wore a dark green muslin confection with lots of lace - very unpractical and frivolous - which he'd given her for her birthday and which she kept for leisurely breakfasts. She liked dressing up, and it was easier to achieve this in the morning when it was a matter of making toast and coffee than when dinners had to be got ready. The division of labour was that Francis fed the cats. Both were in attendance this morning, Lewis was lying full length in the sun, his black sleek fur looked silvery where the light caught each separate, well-groomed hair, his eyes were slits of emerald, as he basked. Amy, round, small and tabby, sat on Alice's lap, purring whenever Alice stroked her. Both were pleased with themselves most of the time.

"What will you do for lunch?" Alice asked.

"Go to the pub, I expect. Don't worry about that. What time will you be back?"

"I'm not sure. It depends on how much time I'll have to spend at the Folly," - Alice's preferred name for Marion House. It had been endowed by Henry Rycourt in the twenties as a home for retired members of the artistic professions - with a few other high-flown sentiments - in memory of his wife; some said in gratitude for her demise. Anyway, he'd called it after her, endowed it liberally and efficiently, then taken himself and the rest of his millions abroad. He'd died some time in the forties having returned to live as riotously as might be with the assembled eccentrics in the house through the war. He'd left a very good further endowment, and his executors had formed a committee of management, of which Alice had been first a member then Chairman for the last two years.

Stella insisted on lunch at a wine bar.

"I must accustom myself to civilization," she said. Her right arm was stiff, but she managed to use a stick, her left arm was still in a sling.

Her ribs were painful, but having stated this fact she made no complaints except to say that all she wanted was to be well enough to go to the hairdressers.

"Oh - they'll see to that for you," Alice reassured her. Now it had come to the point Stella was as nervous as if she was going to a first performance of one of her works.

"It's not exile, you know," Alice said, "we're near, and they're looking forward to having you." "Really looking forward?" Stella liked to have a new audience. Alice was banking on that. Stella had had, it was generally believed, many rather grand lovers, all mysterious as she never denied and never corroborated, but strewed little clues about in her conversations. "When I was in Russia with – ", "When he and I were in the Sahara...", "That time in Ceylon," and various names of small places in romantic countries figured, along with whichever hero was the subject of the story. They were mostly performers or conductors, but all well known enough, even if by now half forgotten by the public, to be remembered by other musicians, although 'before your time' as she would say to younger listeners. She herself was thought to be in her late seventies; she'd been successfully vague about the date of her birth, but she was, by now, nearing the point of adding rather than subtracting years. She had written a number of quartets, some larger works, one famous song cycle, settings of poems by Emily Dickinson, and enough of this and that, concertos and film music, to be more than a cult figure, and she was admired and feared by two generations of pupils.

She was tall, thin as a snake, her black hair, still blackish, in a bun at the back of her neck, as it had been in her famous portrait, her clothes brilliant in colour, haphazard in assembly, so that she looked like some aged Ruritanian princess in flight from a revolution - cloaks, violet, emerald and crimson played a great part in this effect. She enjoyed it when her pupils called her Star (her grandest lover was said to have done this), but most of her older friends firmly used her real name, Stella Fortescue. Don Fortescue had been one of her youthful mistakes.

She had written incidental music for one of Francis's radio plays, and she'd set some of his poems. He'd liked the incidental music but, flattered by her wish to set his *Mirror Poems*, he'd been horrified by the result, for none of the words could be distinguished in her 'wild scoops and screams' - as he described it to Alice after the first rehearsal. The critics, who respected Stella, had praised the sequence, and Francis had realised that concern for the words of songs, rather than concern for the musical ideas they sparked off, was not in her mind. In spite of that their friendship flourished. Alice found her gentler than did Francis. She talked more to her about her feelings than her thoughts; to Francis she presented the self she had invented and, it must be said, perfected. Alice knew that she was lonely, afraid of old age, afraid of losing her invention, ached with rheumatism, found it hard to buy comfortable shoes, and deeply disliked her only daughter who now lived in Australia and had, she quoted crossly, 'dwindled into a wife'. Stella found both Alice and Francis very good friends; she loved Alice, who was kind, gentle and who had grown more beautiful than she had been as a girl, and was no fool. With Francis, she flirted, gossiped, and reported all sorts of dark and scandalous rumours which she credited to reliable sources. Sometimes they were true. What with one thing and another, it was fair for them to give up that Saturday to her.

So, there they were, Alice and Stella, comforting each other in the wine bar; Alice for putting her into an institution (Stella's description of the plan), Stella for requiring so much reassurance. However, when they arrived Stella cheered up considerably. Marion's is a large early Victorian house, still with a garden enclosing it from the world; her room was large, pleasingly furnished and with a bowl of roses on the dressing table. Matron was clearly a woman of character who was not going to be over-impressed by Stella or her reputation or her case of malt whisky, or her complete set of Proust in French, which were the most obvious parts of her luggage. There were two suitcases as well.

"I'll send Lalla to help you unpack," she said, and "then she can bring you some tea. See if you feel equal to coming down for dinner, if not, you can have it up here - tonight." She added the last word firmly, so that Stella should realise it was a concession, and must not be something expected every day.

"Well, Alice, it's not so bad, so far. When shall I see the other inmates?"

"Stella, please, they're known as the Residents."

"Oh well, inmates, playmates - what's the difference? I don't suppose I shall know anyone here."

"You may have met some of them, but they're all dying to see you..." At that moment a slight, fragile-looking girl came in - Asian, possibly Sri Lankan, Stella thought, remembering with a sudden pang her long ago adventure in the island.

"I'm Lalla, Dame Stella, can I unpack for you?" It was a very pretty voice, no trace of a foreign accent.

Stella's attention was immediately engaged. "Thank you my dear, yes, that would be lovely. Alice, run along now. Tell Francis to come to see me soon." She was dismissive, but remembered to say "Thank you for lunch, for bringing me here," before they kissed formally.

Alice ran downstairs and looked in at Matron's office.

"Bless you for having her," she said, "I hope it'll be all right."

Mrs. Miles laughed. "I think so, I'm rather looking forward to it, and of course the Residents are all agog."

"She does swear rather a lot, sometimes."

"They'll adore that, either because they'll feel liberated by it or they'll be enjoyably shocked. Don't worry, Alice, she's going to be all right, and I can see that she needs taking care of. Are you going home at once, or would you like some tea? Some of them are having tea in the garden and they'd love to see you."

Alice knew that if she stayed she'd get entangled. She visited Marion's often enough, and she felt that four hours of Stella had been all she could manage.

"Not today," she said, "bless you all the same. Let me know how it goes."

They parted with mutual goodwill, and Alice got into her car, feeling that perhaps it felt like this when you left a child for its first term at a boarding school, pity, not unmixed with relief once the little victim was out of sight.

She parked the car. There were no garages where they lived, only hotly contested street-parking. As she came through the house she heard voices; Francis, yes, but who was with him? She came through the garden door and saw, of all people, Maria. Maria had been one of her closest friends, a cheerful unromantic hedonist, who had rather faded out of their lives after their marriage, though it was she who had started Francis on his career. It was old history now, and Maria and Charles had lately, improbably, been living in Australia. The friendship had slipped into Christmas letters, shorter and shorter ones at that, without much more than bare news of holidays, or new books or - from Charles and Maria - changes of address.

"Look, look who I've caught," said Francis, getting up as Alice came down the three steps into the garden.

"Oh Maria."

"Alice." They hugged each other, then stood back to look.

Maria had always been a near-beauty; now, after a ten year gap she was lovely, golden brown, brilliant in her scarlet dress, bare armed, golden ear-ringed, radiant and dazzling. Alice, tired and looking thin beside this glowing creature, felt herself warmed and cheered by her presence. Francis said that Alice looked as if she could do with some tea, and went off to make it for them all.

"Alice, Alice - still doing good works? I hoped that marriage had cured you of all that."

"And you were so set against us getting married."

Light as a weathercock, Maria answered that it had seemed unnecessary lunacy to her, but obviously it had not been.

"Francis still looks so young," she said, as if surprised. "His hair is still that funny strawy colour, his eyes are so bright. Of course when people have that sort of goldy-brown skin they do look younger than they are... and that sort of blue shirt..."

Alice supposed that Maria thought that she chose Francis's shirts for him. She was amused and a little annoyed.

"But you look just the same," Maria went on, "tidy and kind and rather like a Botticelli girl."

"After all this time? Well, I feel rather more like - like a hard-hearted parent." She started to talk about Stella.

"Why on earth do you do all this? It sounds like mortification."

Alice looked at her, suddenly realising that she didn't like her at that moment, feeling guilty at the same time, for surely the right attitude would be welcome, as it had been at the instant of recognition, a recall of past liking, of amusing times shared, indeed of past kindnesses of Maria's, not least her perception in helping Francis to his first success. She was deeper in dislike than she suspected, but on as light a level as she could manage she said, "I admire courage..." then realising what a huge and complex subject that would be to explain to Maria, she added, "Stella's a friend, and fun, and I've got a car..." She hoped that Francis would come back quickly, but he was having the usual trouble with the watched kettle that never boils.

"Well, oddly enough, I know her daughter. Stella gave her the hell of a life. So I've not so much time for Stella."

Alice did revive at this bit of information. She'd long learned that truth, if perceived from any point, is likely to turn out to be octagonal or prismatic, and, fond as she was of her, she well knew that Stella's truths were very well edited.

Then there was the happy rattle of china, and Francis appeared with a tray of comfort.

Lapsang smelling deliciously smoky in her cup, Alice revived. "Maria knows Stella's daughter."

"What's she like? We've been given to understand that she's a neurotic little creature, married to a boring Mr. Right."

"Soberly true," said Maria, "but no wonder she's neurotic, that woman destroyed her."

"But she found Mr. Right," said Francis, trying to change the tone. He and Maria had been having a very pleasant hour together before Alice arrived. He found her amusing and he was amused, too, because he remembered some old song about a girl - 'O she was a fire-ship. . .' How did it go on? The rest of it eluded him maddeningly, but a fire-ship she certainly was. And Alice, whether she realised it or not, didn't care for a fire-ship sailing into her life. He felt her reaction, and though this was slightly disquieting, he could not help feeling that it might be fun to have Maria around. Alice kicked off her shoes, had a second cup of tea, and asked where Charles was. All settled into calm as Alice became interested in Maria's account of where and what she'd been doing with the intervening years, and how madly successful Charles had become in his enterprises, all of which were quite incomprehensible to Alice, and nearly so to Francis. Though, from what Maria said, some of them sounded as if they might be questionable.

Stella meanwhile had settled for dinner in her room. She was tired, but the blissful peace of a room with satisfactory proportions and pleasant furniture and, even more, the pleasure of not having other people in other beds around her, made her content. Lalla had been deft: all her belongings that should be put away were put away, her books were within reach, so was the whisky. Dinner had been delicious, lemon chicken, with new potatoes, tomato salad decorated with basil, and then strawberries; enough to make the hospital food fade to a blur of fish fingers and things buried in custard, instead of being, as they had been, a daily grievance. "I think I'm going to enjoy it here," she said to herself, pushing away the thought of her damaged hands, her still aching ribs. Lalla came back at ten, and helped her to bed.

"What are you doing here?" Stella asked her.

"Learning." Lalla in turn asked how Stella had managed to do her hair in hospital, which changed the subject easily.

"Oh, awful," said Stella. "They plaited it in two plaits. Can you imagine? Pigtails. But someone did it for me this morning, nearly properly. I do want a hairdresser more than anything."

"Easy. I'll arrange it. Tomorrow afternoon?"

"Oh, how lovely, how lovely." Stella settled herself on to her pillows with a groan of pleasure. "It's not bad for an institution," she said sleepily, "not at all bad. You must tell why you are here, tomorrow. Please put out the lamp. I don't want to read tonight."

"Goodnight, Dame Stella." Lalla closed the door very quietly.

Lalla went downstairs; some of the Residents were sitting up rather later than usual, for most of them went to their rooms to watch news on their own televisions. They were playing some card game. Lalla wasn't sure what, but it came to an end as she crossed the room to shut the window overlooking the garden.

"Years ago," Liz Grindel said, "there would have been a lot of moths in here - attracted by the light," she explained to the others who had long ago forgotten about moths.

"Well, I suppose there would have been," Mary Carmichael agreed. "They were a great nuisance." "They were very beautiful," Liz Grindel contradicted, "if you took the trouble to look at them." "Taking trouble, taking trouble, why should I take trouble; trouble takes me, and far too often." Viv Reynolds reached for her stick. "I shall go to bed, and if you ask me, that's trouble enough." She laughed in a grim way, and with a barking 'goodnight' she hobbled away, but, as she shut the door she heard Henry de Vos saying to Liz, "What do you expect? She lost 40p, and she does hate to lose at cards."

"We all hate to lose," Mary Carmichael said.

"Not much left to lose, is there?" Henry's question needed no answer.

"Tell me about the moths," Lalla said. "What were they like?"

"I remember the hawkmoths," Liz answered, "privet hawkmoths and humming-bird hawkmoths, I think they were called, rose-pink and green, and there were a lot of brownish, rather furry ones, and sometimes ones that looked like greeny-white lace if they settled on the outside of the window pane and you saw them from inside. I never knew their names. But they were beguilingly mysterious. All night creatures are, I think, today creatures, like us, and I miss them. But you were a night creature yourself, Henry," she added. Henry had been an actor, Liz a painter till her hands had become too arthritic to manage her brushes.

Being described as a night-creature seemed flattering to Henry. He recreated himself as a dashing young man, dancing at night clubs, though usually he had gone home to a flat in Earls Court, and had a modest nightcap with his wife. She had died five years ago. He still missed her when he remembered her.

"Well, yes, you could say that. But now, Lalla, now, nightlife has little attraction, bed, and a good book..."

He looked forward to the nightcap all the same, and he too drifted towards the lift, towards his library book, his striped pyjamas, and the bottle of port which was his favourite tipple.

This left Liz, Mary, Lalla, and Sue and William Hatchett in the room.

"Would you like me to make you some tea?" Lalla asked.

"Please, please," they all spoke at once. So another of their days ended.

Francis came to see Stella the following afternoon. He found her in the garden, tea was over, as they had it rather early at Marion's.

"How are you?" She knew that what he really wanted to know was how she'd faced meeting the others at lunchtime.

"They were rather friendly," she said. "I don't know if I shall actually like any of them, but of course I ought to know more about them. Appearances in old age are misleading. Lots of people look duller than they are."

"An old friend of ours came to see us yesterday evening. She's just back from Australia and said she'd met your daughter. I thought she was called Joanna, but Maria kept calling her Désirée..."

"Oh dear, silly bint." Stella looked shocked. "I'd forgotten about that. You see, Don - I was married to him still when she was born - wanted to call her Felicity, and that was going too far for me so I capped it, for, goodness, how she wasn't desired, to be just, by either of us. But he'd fallen for her; she was, in all fairness, a pretty infant, and he took it seriously and rushed off to register her, but it didn't seem right to let her be stuck with that. Even Don came to his senses after he'd done the deed, so we always called her Joanna. I can't remember why. Désirée, my God, she's even stupider than I realised. She does write postcards sometimes, but she signs them 'J'."

"Well, that's the answer then," Francis said. "I thought perhaps there was an unmentioned twin."

"There's a woman here who has twins, quite old now, quite terribly old. They are both ambassadors. She told me all about them at the moment of our meeting. She's got a husband too, looks like a tortoise.

They're called Hatchett; blunt ones, I'd say."

"Go on," said Francis.

"Then another couple. They call each other darling all the time and throw looks of hate at each other. It's an edged sword, that word. Do you call Alice darling? I've never heard you do so."

He wasn't going to tell her that in particular closeness he called her Alice - no more - it was a tone of voice. Darling was a social address nowadays he thought, though yes, he did call her darling sometimes. Then, damn her impertinence, she's always trying to find out ... find out what? Something to think about. His thoughts were covered by silence. But Stella was pattering on with her first impressions.

"They've all got pasts," she said. "I don't know if they were ever real. I mean I know some of their names, they've the sort of names one has heard, but don't seem real to me. More like people in a bad novel, you're told they did this and that, but you can't imagine them actually doing it. Sitting and writing? Going to rehearsals, playing 'cellos? Yes. It's sort of soap opera stuff, curtain calls, and parties after first nights. No misery, or uncertainty, or urgency."

"Well Stella, you've only been here for twenty four hours; you can't expect them to tell you ALL in that sort of time, though you seem to have heard quite a lot."

"I don't think that there's anything to tell."

"Their works? Of course if it's all performers, it's damned unfair. They can't do whatever it was now because they're incapacitated. You have words to speak for you."

At this she looked gratified, and told him that she was to give a television interview before a Prom performance.

"Marvellous," he said, glad that she should have this publicity. "What are you going to wear?"

"I thought that crimson cloak. The Indian wool, you know, with the gold sort of paisley shapes on it." Diverted, she talked about what she was going to say in the interview, the work that was to be played, and the conductor.

Francis half heard what she said. The sunlight was making wonderful patterns in the leaves of the ash tree at the end of the garden, and that set him thinking about witches, and then about the other residents, trying to see them through Stella's eyes. Then wondering how they looked to the young, to Lalla, to the Matron in charge of their ills and their decrepit bodies, and back to witches as Stella said, "I'll have to have some help to get on to the platform."

"Oh," he said, laughing, "Stella, you could go on a broomstick."

"What are you talking about?"

"I was thinking about witches, about how appearances disguise people, how your crimson cloak would stream out as you sailed over the Albert Memorial and how it would astonish the Prommers."

"What publicity." Stella liked the idea immensely. "Seriously though, if you and Alice are coming to the concert, would you help me on to the stage?"

"The BBC will surely give you a glamorous escort?" She brightened at this.

"I suppose they will. I think I'll go in now. We have dinner so very early, and I've invited that Mrs. Carmichael, she's my next door neighbour, to have a drink. So I'd better be there. And Francis, do you know about that girl Lalla? Why's she here? She's a mystery to me, and far too pretty to be among all of us old things."

"Lalla? We met her at a party in the spring. She read English at Cambridge, and she was filling in time doing any job she could find, so Alice nobbled her."

"She's about, if you know what I mean. She unpacked, and she helped me go to bed, and I saw her doing the flowers, and she was here and there. She's a love, but she never, never talks about herself."

"She told Alice and me, fairly soon after we first met her: her family is Sri Lankan. They were all the kind that were educated in England and got double firsts or double blues or both, and became judges or international scholars. They lived in marvellous houses and, of course, later on, they were all drawn into politics. Her parents died in some epidemic and she was brought up by grandparents. She was an only child. I think her parents were young when they died, as the grandparents weren't very old. Then there was some awful political crisis and her grandfather was murdered, and her grandmother went into a sort of nunnery. And her uncles got Lalla out of the country, and to England. They're the sort of family who have lots of friends here; it was boarding school and Cambridge. There's not much money left. I think she has a tiny income, and she's doing some research with her young man. He read history, and she says that he's quite a good painter."

Francis didn't want Stella to feel that she was being researched so he was vague as he helped her to her feet and offered her his arm as they talked. She said, "I can't, must use my stick," so he put his arm round her waist as a sort of support.

It was so long since anyone had put an arm round her so naturally that she was amazed by a sudden longing to put her head on his shoulder, to cry, to be young, to be aware of her body as something more than an unmanageable mass of aches and deficiencies, that she was shocked by these unexpected re-awakenings of longing for naked flesh against her own.

"Can you manage?" he asked, unaware of the ghosts and memories he had charmed from a winter sleep.

So Lalla had come to Marion's for a summer job. It was also part of her research project. She and Tom, both doing post-graduate work at Cambridge, had been driving back after a picnic and seen an old man lying in long grass by a country bus stop. They had hurried to see if he was all right, half thinking that he might be a drunk, or just have fallen asleep while waiting for a bus, and dreading to find that he had had a stroke, for neither had a crumb of medical knowledge or first aid training. He had tripped, he told them, twisted his foot and could not move. The bus driver had not seen him where he'd fallen, and had driven past. He'd been there for a couple of hours, and feared that he might be there all night. Tom and Lalla helped him into the car and took him to hospital. They had liked him immediately, he was modest about the pain he felt, courteous, and funny about this accident. They visited him several times, and were distressed when they found that on his discharge from hospital he had been taken into an old people's home. Tom had volunteered to fetch his belongings from his lodgings, and both he and Lalla had become regular visitors. Sometimes they collected him for drives into the country. He was a great talker, and obviously glad of a chance to tell his stories to people interested in the ghost stories he knew, and between the three of them they'd written a long article on his life, the many changes he had lived through as an agricultural worker, as a soldier and as a builder's labourer. This had excited both Tom, as an historian, and Lalla as a beginner at social work, and on the strength of their writing they had been commissioned to write a book on how old people adapted to living in communal groups, old people's homes of one kind and another. To Alice, who had met Lalla at a drinks party, it all sounded rather vague and improbable, but she had liked Lalla immediately.

"Aren't you rather young to undertake this sort of research?" she asked.

"Yes, we are," Lalla said, "but I knew all my grandparents well, and I think there's too much segregation of age groups. I learned so much from my relations, and they were fun, too, though I only saw them in the holidays. I even knew my great grandmother."

Alice was immediately interested.

"My husband worked with someone, not unlike your discovery. He was called William, and he must have been a remarkable man. I never met him, though, so I knew him only by what Francis wrote about him."

"Ours is called Fred. He's very much a countryman. In fact he's someone who could have stepped out of Shakespeare. I can hear him saying, 'Charles' wain is over the new chimney and yet our horse not packed.'"

Alice laughed. "At least there aren't any fleas in the home. That must have made travellers' lodgings a misery and probably not only travellers' lodgings."

They were pleased with each other. Alice didn't like Falstaff much, but she was fond of all his pub and campaign friends, much like characters she had come across in her social work days. So their reality was never in doubt as far as she was concerned. A solid, unchanging band of citizenry surviving all time's changes, who were at home in any century.

"What are you doing, now?" she asked.

"Looking for a job that will allow me to go on with our book."

"Would a temporary one be any help?"

"Yes, indeed it would, the best thing possible. Tom has to go to America for a couple of months. He's got an American grandmother, and there's some sort of family business - and," she added, "we thought a glance at the sunset homes wouldn't come amiss."

"Can you come to supper on Sunday? I'll have a talk with the Matron at a place I'm concerned with. They need some extra help through the summer when the staff have holidays. Nothing medical - that's always covered - but general helping about the place. Would it interest you if I can arrange it?"

"Certainly it would. And, Mrs. Dulac, nothing would be more exciting for Tom than meeting your husband. He's a great admirer."

"Oh, good, eight o'clock, then? And I'll talk with Mrs. Miles. Let's hope that it comes off."

"Thank you, thank you, said Lalla. They drifted apart, Lalla to say goodbye, and to hasten to Tom to bring him this good news, Alice to talk with other acquaintances for a little longer. On the way home she told Francis of this echo pattern, his William's memory and Lalla's living Fred, both enriching young beginners in life.

"I thought that she looked remarkably pretty," Francis said, "but I got whisked away to the other end of the room; Gerard was insistent, and I had to talk to some of his Dutch friends."

"Yes, I saw that rescue was impossible. But you weren't looking bored. I've asked her to supper on Sunday. Her young man apparently read your Meredith book at school, and he admires 'Modern Love' as much as you do."

"That will be common ground, anyway." Francis liked the idea of meeting Lalla properly, and prepared to hear about her projects as Alice was so pleased to have found her for Marion's. Literary talk with her young man, he thought, might be tiresome.

In the event, Lalla came alone, for Tom had promised to spend the evening with some Cambridge friends who had invited them both. After discussion he agreed that she must go to the Dulacs though he could not disentangle himself from the other engagement, much as he wanted to meet Francis. "People should not live without telephones," he said.

"It saves money, and they're always broke. But, if I get the job," Lalla said, "I'm sure you'll be asked when you come back."

"Then you must get the job."

A meeting with Mrs. Miles and a visit to Marion's was arranged for Lalla, and everything was settled quickly, so she had been installed for the summer as soon as Tom had gone off to America.

Lalla was sitting in her room at Marion's. It was at the top of the house, an attic with a sloping ceiling. She imagined it as it had been when two housemaids might have slept on narrow iron bedsteads, with hooks behind the door for their dresses, perhaps a yellowish wooden wash hand stand with a heavy jug and basin, perhaps a dressing table to match with a swinging mirror wedged with folded paper to keep it still. It amused her to transform the room back to its old appearance.

Now it was pale pink, curtains and bed cover dark blue, white furniture, honeysuckle in a vase on the bed table scenting the air. She was writing to Tom. He was having a holiday with his grandmother who lived in Annapolis, and though she was rather too lively to count as an object for study, and though it was a duty visit, it was certainly a pleasant break for him. He wrote enthusiastically, of the pretty town, the sea, the seafood, idleness. She was writing about Stella, less an answer to his last letter than an exploration of this newcomer to Marion's.

"She's the first person I've met here who has a present that's still active. She'd be hell to live with, I think, because, quite properly, she thinks of her work and it comes, vividly, first in her life. I compare her to a sea bird. Land exists as a roosting place, but her music is her sea. We're the cliffs, and she doesn't spend much time or thought on anyone, except peripherally, as her present perch. It's interesting, I think it's because she, and only she among those here, has a future to look forward to. I'm leaping to conclusions though, after a week, and there'll be lots more to find out. She's trapped by her inabilities and infirmities, much more than the rest of them who've arrived at their old ages to find just what they expected in a sort of way, though no one is as consistent as that. They keep on surprising me with flashes of what they used to be. Suddenly I imagine old Henry de Vos as Paris, a rather young suitor, never a Romeo. And then, there he is, complaining about the biscuits, or having a headache because he had a nightcap too many and he can't afford good port.

"Incidentally, I went to 'Love's Labour's Lost' in the Park last night. I wish you'd been there. It's such a marvel to know that none of them will ever be any older. The young men will go on for ever being silly and wonderful and beguiled. And I suppose the girls will have a dreadful year being in court mourning, and then there'll be a reunion, and marriages. Or will they have thought things over and all marry older Frenchmen? I wonder, I wonder, but of course they won't. It will be beginning over again for ever.

"Darling, it's lovely weather here, and I miss you. I do look forward to our holiday, but there's so much summer to get through first, and without you. I'll write more about Dame Stella in a much more professional way. Liz Grindel is into acid rain, and the greenhouse upper-atmosphere, and the Hatchetts are expecting a visit from their son and his wife who always cancel their visits at the last moment. Mr. and Mrs. Dulac come to see Dame S. Hell, there's the bell, I must rush to the other end of the house.

"Love and love, L."

Lalla rushed. It was Liz Grindel who couldn't undo a parcel that had come for her. "Too much sticky tape," she grumbled. "It looks as if no one wants it unpacked." Her scissors were blunt, anyway, so Lalla fetched a kitchen knife and finally got the parcel opened for her. It was books again, ecological horror stories, Henry called them. He was an entirely urban man, and teased Liz whenever they happened to be in the garden at the same time, by calling everything by its wrong name. Clematis he firmly described as laburnum. Roses as hollyhocks, and so on. She told Lalla, who was unwrapping these new paperbacks, that Mary Carmichael had said that he did it to tease her.

"She said that he'd go on as long as I rose to it every time. Why should he want to tease me, Lalla?"

"Perhaps because you're a serious person, Mrs. Grindel, and Mr. de Vos couldn't be called serious"

"That he's not," said Liz Grindel, much pleased at Lalla's recognition of her seriousness. She went on talking as she piled the books on top of others on a shelf.

"You see my dear, people who have lived through as much as we have, my generation, ought to be serious." Just then Mary Carmichael knocked, opened the door. "May Minette and I come in?"

Minette was her dog, an old and sedate Cavalier, dark chestnut with solemn brown eyes, the only beneficiary of the firmly laid down rule that no one who lived at Marion's should have to give up their pets on being accepted as a Resident. Luckily the Matron, who had her own dog, liked animals. Equally luckily no one else had any animals. Minette was a general favourite, exploiting her undoubted charm to profit by illicit biscuits, cakes and grapes in such a discreet way that her owner often did not see her successes and worried when she didn't finish her official dinner.

"Oh Mary, Lalla and I were talking about Henry being so frivolous for his age."

"Were you now?" Mary sat down with a sigh of comfort. Liz had two very comfortable armchairs.

"Do you suppose," Liz went on with her train of thought, "do either of you suppose that if it became known that the world was in frightful danger, as it is," she spoke severely, "of perishing because of this poisonous layer in the upper atmosphere..."

"She's simplifying for us," Lalla thought.

"...that people would be prepared to stop using petrol and diesel to save us all? No cars, nothing. Would they?"

"Of course not, Liz," Mary answered briskly. "You know that as well as

I do. And anyway they'd perish just as soon if there was no way of moving food supplies about."

"Organization is always possible if it's necessary," Liz said grandly, temporarily closing the subject. "Lalla, be a love and get out the sherry."

As Lalla moved to the cupboard where Liz kept glasses and bottles Minette sidled up to her. She knew the word sherry was synonymous with some delicious cheesy biscuits and she had every intention of assisting Lalla with those.

"Minette, don't push," said Lalla in such a loving voice that Minette took her words for praise and pushed her arm even more so that she did indeed drop two little biscuits from the tin she had opened ready to put them in their usual blue glass bowl.

"You horrible dog," said Lalla in an even more loving voice. It was she who combed Minette, took her for walks, and did all she could to make the rather boring old-lady life she had with Mary entertaining.

The other two were back at a conversation about Henry. They were both slightly in love with him and competed for his attention. Of this he was well aware, and, like Minette, was on the look out for profit. Like her, he liked the time of day for sherry and sociability and it was a very few minutes before he joined the party. Liz was the lucky possessor of a nephew in the wine business who was fond of her and so she was always rather better provided than most of the others with desirable bottles.

"You'll stay and have a drink, Lalla?"

"Thank you, I'd love to, but I must catch the post. Can I take letters for anyone?"

No one had written any so she went with hers to Tom, and Minette went with her, leaving the three oldest inhabitants to their gossip.

As soon as the door closed behind her they started to talk about Stella.

"I'm sorry, in a way, that she's not going to stay," Liz said. "It's cheering to be with someone who is still mixed up with things outside here."

"But did you hear how she talked of those people at the BBC? I mean that man who is so nice on Sunday morning? Well, she's probably met him, I suppose, but all that - well, I'm as broadminded as anyone, but - should one? It's not like just saying things when..."

"I didn't hear that, but he is rather like an old tea bag, I agree." Mary had liked the comparison.

"I don't like her music anyway," Liz raised her eyebrows.

"I didn't know you'd been exposed to much of it."

"Need one hear much of anything one doesn't like?"

Mary absentmindedly held out her glass. Henry filled it for her. He had not so far contributed. Now he said, faintly maliciously, "I think that it's good to see a woman dramatise herself. She looks wonderful in that emerald green affair, as if she'd just left her kingdom." The two he was with tended to wear unnoticeable colours.

"If she had a kingdom to leave..." Mary often did not finish her sentences, leaving others to surmise what the end of her thought might have been, had she reached it.

This set Henry to thinking of kingdoms. He had a sort of view of himself as an exile, and, if you are going to be an exile, he fancied you must be an exiled monarch, or perhaps a great professor. He did not think of himself as a victim in any way, nor as a failure, but as someone who had other and nobler rights than those conferred by being at Marion's. He did not define, but at the back of his mind lay a sad insufficiency. Never Hamlet, never Lear, never even Romeo all those years ago. He had been happy enough with his wife, but her death had been less of a shock than a cause of problems for him.

Marion's, or rather the Committee, had come to his rescue. They were always thankful to find aged, tolerably distinguished men as there were so many widows of the distinguished and deceased. Men, it was observed, cheered the ladies, who competed for their friendship, their escort, their attention, so Henry had been accepted gratefully and had lived there for five years. Liz and Mary had been there for just over four, and the three of them had found a certain compatibility, though, as Matron frequently observed, being of an age did not necessarily constitute any kind of bond. It was lucky if some of the Residents did find some common ground other than that of being infirm and being over eighty, so she encouraged such sociabilities and did all she could to see that the one reliable pleasure left to them all, delicious meals, were to be relied on.

Chapter 2

Alice that week had other preoccupations than Stella's welfare. Maria's return had been a surprise. She had got out of the way of thinking of her, though when she and Francis were first married, and indeed in the years before their marriage, she and Maria had seen each other a great deal and had been closely allied in friendship. Maria had always been able to travel. She had married the successful Charles when she was very young, she'd never had a job, rather, fingers in many pies, interest and pleasure in causing people useful to each other to meet, a generally decorative benevolence. Alice's sphere had been more modest as a professional social worker, exploring a world of which she was not a native, but doing so with a decent intention of finding ways in which unacceptable situations could be resolved, problems that were not too appalling solved, any odd bits of help given where resources for such help could be found. Soon after marriage she had felt that she couldn't do the work any more. To do it well, and to do it all the time, drained her capacities. Too many sorrows, deprivations and hopelessnesses had filled her days as the world seemed to be getting harder and harder for more and more people. She had a bad conscience about resigning, when the need seemed greater than ever, but Francis worried over her worries and she'd worried about him worrying. At the moment when she was wondering about alternatives Maria had asked her if she knew anyone who could work for one of her friends who sold furniture. Someone, said Maria, who knows enough about good furniture of the eighteenth and early nineteenth century to enjoy the work. Alice had heard her voice saying, "What about me?"

"Alice, how marvellous." And in a day or two her prospects changed. She gave her notice, felt badly about the web of darkness she abandoned, and began to re-enjoy herself among beautiful and desirable things.

Francis felt that such a change was entirely reasonable. He worked at home and had done so since he'd given up his job in an ironmongery shop, which had been his stop-gap after Cambridge. It had served a double purpose. He felt that he was exploring real life, because he had got to know the people with whom he worked, selling all sorts of hardware in Camden Town, and it provided him with enough money to live in a bed-sitting room of a dingy kind while he tried to become a writer. On his half-days of early-closing freedom he had explored London. He had, like many of his contemporaries, had vacation jobs before, and while he was being a postman one Christmastime, he had become acquainted with Alice's great uncle and aunt who had cheered his morning round with cups of coffee. He had met Alice at this time, not through her relations, oddly enough, but through mutual friends, and he had given her a kitten he had rescued. One thing had led to another in a way that had seemed haphazard at the time. His old colleague at the ironmongers had died in hospital after an accident, and Francis, who had spent as much time as he was able with him, was there at his death. From that experience came a long poem which Alice had typed for him. Maria had read it, and swept it off to give to one of her friends. A broadcast followed, and Francis began his career. Still, as he said, he'd gone on being an ironmonger for a while.

Alice had liked going out to work; it suited her orderly nature to have two different patterns in her life. The furniture shop lasted for ten years, then the ownership changed, and she felt she'd explored that world enough. She'd become involved with Marion's very slightly already and very soon after giving up work in the shop she'd become Chairman of the Committee, and as by then Francis was making enough money for them both to live on, she'd stopped having a job and had started to delight in her freedom and in having time for pottering and for gardening in a casual way. She'd always done most of his typing and with this she continued.

At first when Maria teased her about reverting to good works she had taken little notice, but as Maria spoke of it every time they met, Alice became irritated. Francis said, "I expect it's because she wishes she could do the same."

"Shall I let her loose in Marion's Bedlam?"

"No. Not if you want to stay on as their support and prop and all that."

"Yes I do. There are a few things that I shall probably have to fight for there, things that could go by default rather easily."

"You've been saying that for years, Alice."

"It's always true: The utter boringness of eternal vigilance, and the trouble that comes if one misses one's argus-eyed wakefulness."

"I shouldn't," said Francis, "worry about Maria. She'll soon find other things to do."

He worried about her quite a lot. He hadn't told Alice that he'd lunched with her the day before this talk. Alice had been out, anyway, and he'd been meaning, as he did sometimes, to have a pub lunch. Maria had telephoned. She said that she would like to talk to him about an idea she'd had, and he'd gone to lunch at her new flat. Charles didn't mind where they lived and liked hotels, so when they had anywhere more permanent the interiors were all Maria's invention and extravagance. This one was just off Rosslyn Hill.

Her idea was, oddly, based on Marion's. She wanted to do a programme about Stella. She had television friends everywhere and Stella was old enough and distinguished enough to be acceptable, "probably rather late at night," she explained.

"But you said that you hadn't any time for her," he expostulated

"Well, I've thought about it, and I heard the songs, yours, I mean, that cycle, and I found them enough to make me re-consider Désirée and her wrongs. She isn't interesting enough to be the sort of daughter Stella ought to have had. Now," she went on briskly, "I want your help."

"Alice's would be more to the point."

"That too, but not yet. I know you can't write poems to order, but it strikes me that your first thing of all, about the old man you knew, leads in to this. Could you help me with some sort of script? About old age and how people live when they've outlived..."

"Stella is still working."

"Yes, I suppose so, but all the same, it would be interesting to see how someone like that copes with being old, and if it's you, she'll probably agree?"

They talked about it more while they had lunch and over coffee.

"I'll think about it," he promised. Ideas were being sparked off as he spoke, a familiar vague turmoil with sentences rising like foam-caps on breakers. He wanted to get home, to get to paper and pen, to try to find a shape for the whole thing. It seemed suddenly the completion of his affection for Stella, for the goodness and silliness of the history of the home, for Alice's work there. And it would involve him in working with Maria. All these strands drew together. He thanked her for lunch. They kissed goodbye at the sitting room door, and again at the front door, and for rather longer there. Maria's scent was extremely attractive, her arm round his neck delightfully natural, her spark had struck fire in his mind, and he didn't want to have to say anything explicit to Alice till he'd worked alone. Later, later, the explanations and plans must come, but after the words. He put down his cup; tea indoors today, as it had rained most of the afternoon.

"Work," he said, "I've got a glimmer of something." He kissed Alice in friendly greeting, and he went off to his desk.

> Small encampments on the shores of death,
> strangers gathered in a shared delay...

He knew then, at once, it would never be a programme about Marion's or about Stella, but it would become his exploration of age.

"Lalla has cheered the place up," Mrs. Miles had said to Alice. "She's far the prettiest person they see and she seems to find things in common with all the Residents in an almost uncanny way, and she's extraordinarily patient." Lalla herself had become easily friendly with Alice, and she would come in to see her sometimes. She always telephoned first to discover if Alice had time to spare.

"I've brought Minette. I do hope you don't mind," Lalla said. "She's getting too fat. I found the Petersons giving her chocolates." Alice laughed. "I know about that. Their daughter gives them boxes and boxes of them and there seem to be a lot of ones with crystallized ginger in them, which they hate and Minette loves."

"Well, crystallized ginger is horrible," Lalla agreed, "and so's Minette's figure. She's so greedy," she added in a loving voice. The cats came in at that moment, and stood contemplating Minette, who wagged her tail in a friendly manner. Amy arched her back and looked at Lewis for guidance. He was the more worldly character, and anyway he recognised Minette from her previous visits as harmless. So he strolled over to her and sat down a yard away. Amy retreated to Alice's lap.

"Dame Stella's gruesomely lonely," Lalla said. "The trouble is that it's not for people so much as for work. It's horrible to see her hands, and know that they're useless for writing. Her mind I suppose is still full of ideas and that faltering three bars or so that she can get onto paper before the pain makes her stop must be frustrating beyond belief."

"That, of course." Alice's own hands almost hurt when she thought of Stella's.

"Most of the others have let go, they have made little cocoons of every day," Lalla said. "But I know that Mary Carmichael sleeps with her husband's photograph under her pillow. When I went in to say goodnight, about a week ago, and she was crying, she said, 'You must think I'm an old fool, but I miss him so much.' She seemed to think that I'd find it shocking that any one old should cry, or that I wouldn't begin to understand."

"Do you imagine what they were like when they were young?" Alice asked. "It's strange when you're shown photographs to realise it's the same person as the young thing. Mary was very slim, with masses of curly hair. She showed me pictures of herself on a cruise, once, and I've been trying to see how the change happened. There's not a recognisable trace."

"It's bad luck, to be young and in love inside a clumsy body, with thin hair, and full of aches and pains and memories, and to know that no one knows you as you are to yourself. A disappointment every time you look in a looking glass and see a stranger there."

"Or a second self. One must get used to it," Alice said, "and know what to expect every morning." She wondered how soon this would happen to her.

"But to go back to Dame Stella," Lalla said. "There was a great scene at lunch today. She does talk rather louder than the others, you know, and she was telling the Hatchetts about having people in for drinks yesterday. One of them was someone they knew and she said, 'the silly old pouf can't hold his drink any more, and was pissed as a newt.' Incidentally, why newts? And they were horrified and got up and swept out. At least she did. He held the door open for her, and then he came back to finish his pudding. There was a mad babble of conversation to cover up. Half of them were thrilled, half horrified, and she said to him, old Garry Hatchett, 'did your wife feel queer or something?'"

"Oh dear," said Alice, laughing about the pudding, "was it treacle tart?"

"Yes. He does love his puddings."

"Probably the only sweetness and light in his life."

"I'm going to Cambridge tomorrow," Lalla said, "to take our Fred out, if he's well enough to go. I wish he was a retired poet or diplomat or something, and that we could have him at Marion's. I hate to see him sitting around with all the other old men whose lives have ebbed away.

He's got a daughter in Canada, and she writes sometimes, and a nephew up at King's Lynn, but that's not much use to him."

"Lalla, how nice. I hope you're going to see some others as well. It's not much of a change for a day away otherwise."

"Well, yes, I shall see people for dinner. But I do like Fred. He's a great teller of ghost stories. I think I've probably heard them all, but occasionally he produces one I don't know, and I love them."

"What do you tell him?"

"I tell him about Sri Lanka. He was astonished to hear about tapioca growing, he'd no idea, and about Sigyria, and the girls painted on the rocks. I took a picture postcard of them, and he was thrilled. I think he believes I lived with them. And I've only been there once, it's such a hideous trek up those endless steps, but the view is immense, and I love ruined gardens. In fact, we're both romantics, so we tell each other fairy stories, and enjoy them."

Alice asked about Tom, his work and his holiday, and Lalla said that his rich grandmother was spoiling, him. "I wonder if he'll be able to enjoy cheap hotels in Italy after all that," she said.

"Goodness, I'd almost forgotten," Alice got up and fetched a carrier bag. "Here are the guide books I promised to find."

Minette and Amy, who Alice put on the floor, stared at each other. Minette got up, rather stiffly, as if to go to her, but Amy slipped away behind a chair.

"I'd better go now," Lalla said, taking the books. "I shall have a lovely evening looking at these, and I'll probably need it. Supper may be full of dramas, and I'll have to spend a little time with Dame Stella. She's decidedly in the dog-house with several of the other residents, and she'll want to demolish them. Better to me than in public."

"I hope you'll get a good ghost story. You must tell us some of them.

Not when I'm going to be alone in the house, though."

"Oh, they're no good unless they're frightening." Lalla waved from the gate, and Alice stood looking at her roses, and wondering if she should go and do some dead-heading, or if she'd leave that chore till tomorrow.

Having been away from England for so long Maria was finding it difficult to settle down. She wasn't a particularly settling down sort of person anyway, and restless when there was nothing particular to do. She wondered if she should go out, go to look at pictures, swim perhaps? Telephone to Francis? That made her pause. She found that he had become a most attractive man. It was strange to remember him as she had first known him, rather silent, shy, friendly indeed, but not at home with us, she thought. She remembered how Charles had taken charge of everything on the day that Alice and Francis married, and Alice's much-loved great-uncle had died. Charles had been more like a father, or an older brother, she conceded, in the way that he'd fixed everything and bustled them off, saddened and startled by the sudden message that had reached them on the way to the Registrar's office. They looked more like orphans than newly married people, she remembered. And now Francis had many television plays to his credit, as well as his books. It was she who'd started it all, by introductions, she acknowledged, not by being his inspiration. "What a word to use," she thought, "but he is the only poet I've ever known," and such pre-Raphaelite ideas did still drift mistily round the word. She realised that he found her amusing. She found him attractive, but for lunches, she diagnosed, not for dinners. He and Alice appeared to have a most secure, affectionate and easy relationship, as if neither had ever contemplated any other, or indeed any deceptions, evasions, curiosities, or possibilities. For herself, as she had once explained it to Alice when they were much closer friends, when Alice was unmarried and recovering from a disastrous love affair, life was like an illuminated manuscript she'd seen in the British Museum. Charles is the text, very clear, very strong, very solid - "mind you, my Latin isn't up to much, so I'm being figurative about that" - but the border, all sorts of flowers and dragons and fishes twined about the gold curlicues. "That's how I want my life," she said, "solid in the middle and frivolous all round."

Alice had agreed that it sounded a perfect arrangement. But it looked now as if it was Alice that had managed the illuminated page. The borders of her own life had not been so delightfully flowery, nor so fantastic, and the text in the middle of the page was of uncertain value, obscure meaning.

So, in the end she telephoned to Alice, not Francis. "Let's have lunch tomorrow."

Alice, feeling pleased with her day, having dead-headed her roses and answered all her letters, agreed.

Lalla spent the hour in the train from Cambridge writing to Tom.

"I wonder why so many old men are called Fred? Our Fred was much better this time, he's settled down, and there are some new old men in the home. They play pool and they go to the pub on Saturdays. In a way they've got back something they all had when they were in the army. The bad bits of that life have become unreal, and they feel it was a freedom. Well, economically it was, no competition, of course, and not much responsibility, and they could then, as they do now, remember all the un-irking things about their families. A made-up sort of life. They're all doing rather well for each other in spite of feet and bladders and digestions that aren't what they were. Four Freds, two Jacks, one Jumbo and one Nobby. They read the papers too, and it was good to see so much going on. No ghost stories this time, but Fred had one amazing account of a blind man, a friend of his father's, who could tell by the sound the leaves made what each tree was when he went for a walk or sat in a wood. I suppose he'd been doing country work all his young life, and learned to listen, and of course there weren't many extra sounds then. Now, of course, he'd have had a radio and talking books, which would probably be much more diverting, but the other is impressive. Fred is very curious about vultures, I can't think why. He doesn't care for the vicar who comes to visit them, so perhaps he's trying to plan for a tower of silence rather than local burial. He thought that I must, of course, be a heathen, and could tell him more. But I doubt if there are any arrangements of that sort to be made in Cambridge. What birds? Starlings? Magpies?

Don't think they'd be much use.

I stayed the night with Rose and James and the Tiger came to dinner.
Tiger is wanting to see you very much and James had written a play.
Rose says it's good. Liverpool Street. Back to the Bedlam.

I hope no more dramas. Perhaps a letter from you? I'll post this in
the station. Your L."

There hadn't been any drama while she was away either, but when
Lalla went to help Stella in her room she found her abashed. She'd
obviously missed Lalla, and had spent time repenting.

"I have behaved badly," she said as Lalla poured out some whisky for
her. "I'm a guest here, and I ought not to have been difficult." Lalla
noted the well-judged word with amusement.

"No, of course you shouldn't," she said, "but being a guest is a difficult
art, isn't it?"

"Far too difficult for me, and I hate being a bad one, but I'm turning
into a crotchety old shrew - you see it's so ridiculous not being able to
be independent. I hate being so - inept. I doubt if I'll ever be able to
manage to live alone again and the prospect of having someone *always*
about is horrid. One of us would have to be quiet, no radio, I mean,
unless I wanted it, and one of us would have to put up with the other
one's friends. It's all right if there's space, which there isn't, so no one
can ever stay, because there's only the little room, and it's stuffed full
of music, how'd I ever make it liveable-in for another human being's
life? Don't ever get old, Lalla, it's so unsuitable."

"Almost all the poems about old age have been written by young men,"
Lalla said shifting the subject a little. "Except Yeats."

"Yes, and Hardy."

Lalla, who was also having a, rather smaller, whisky, quoted in a
questioning voice:

"The soul's dark cottage, battered and decayed
lets in new life, through chinks that time has made."

"Does it, Dame Stella? It seems to me that that is an odd assumption. From what I've seen people get more so. I mean the light would have been there already, and chinks let in rain as well. But Marvell wasn't old, of course."

"People are what they've always been. That's why I get so petulant. I want to shake this lot up. They've ceased to react. And I don't know why they were so put-about."

"No, no they haven't ceased to react." Lalla was fierce now. "They're all, no, almost all, busy coping with aches and griefs, and lonelinesses. It piles on too much all at once. I think that Alice is right when she talks of courage."

"Give me the barricades any day. At least that'd be a lively death, not a slow dropping off."

Lalla could imagine her on a barricade, a Delacroix figure.

"In your crimson cloak," she agreed, "but good barricades are hard to come by."

"So are good geriatric homes I suppose," said Stella.

"Oh God," said Lalla. "Don't patronise."

Then she held out her hand.

"It's all impossible, isn't it? We think we're doing our best, but how can anyone? It's a last chance, to find all that's been lost, or missed, or wasted, and you're the only one here that's positive, and doing and creating - as you've always done. You've something that none of the others have. So, however awful it is, and I know it's awful, you are different. And so it's probably worst of all for you, but best too." She was crying as she spoke.

Stella was silent, drinking her whisky.

Lalla stood up. "I'm so sorry," she said. "I think I'd better get Matron to help you to bed."

"I'll never forgive you if you do," Stella said. "This has been one of the few worthwhile talks I've had here. You've treated me like a real person again. It's one of the worst things, you know, when people make allowances because one's body is useless supposing that one must be pandered to and lied to. No, you've never lied, but I see it all the time. Stinking allowances for selfish old fools, cosseting morally and mentally. It's unbearable. Help me to bed, be gentle with my stupid body, but always treat me as an equal human."

Lalla told Francis about this when she saw him a few days later.

"There's one thing I've noticed," he said, "and I expect you have too. Some people, in age, become absolutely indistinguishable as male or female, except for their clothes. There's a kind of sexual anonymity as there is with babies. Put a hood or a shawl round their faces and you can't tell. And yet they've each got their whole past as man or woman, as babies have their whole future as man or woman and Stella is very much a woman, to look at, still."

"Oh yes, so's Mary Carmichael. So's Angela. But some of them could be either sex."

"Yes, you're right. I've got to know them as characters, through Alice, so I don't notice their appearances so much I suppose, and I don't see them more often than I need. It's Alice's show, and I go only when I have to." He added, reminiscing "Awful Christmas, sometimes. Alice was telling me about your Fred and his ghost stories. Does he believe in them?"

"Sometimes. But he does love to make the flesh creep. He says a lot of them happened to people he knows, or knew, or his relations knew, I imagine it's the oral tradition again. They're probably local stories and generations old."

"Do you believe in ghosts yourself, Lalla?"

"Yes, of course. I've never seen one, heard one. But I have felt presences, as if none of my senses were sharp enough to see or to hear what must have been there."

"Yes. That's just about it. I'm glad that it's still mysterious." He paused, then he said, as if testing an idea on her. "On one level I think the old are haunted by the ghosts of themselves, of their pasts, of their childhoods. Not fully integrated with all that they have been." Lalla was doubtful. "I see them more as if they can't be themselves any more."

Francis seized on this. "Casting off, do you think? Losing their own reality. Like leaves changing colour before they fall."

"And I suppose," she said, taking this up, "no leaf is much consoled by the thought of next year's buds."

"The tree endures. Where does this leave us with immortality, Lalla?"

"Most of them, C. of E., without thinking about it, particularly if they like the vicar," she said, offering information rather than speculation.

"The C. of E. words, the proper ones, are good incantations."

"Have you written about old age much?"

"No, but now, yes. I thought of a line, 'A small encampment, on the shores of death,'" testing it on her.

"Yes." It struck her as right. She was silent, for a moment, imagining all the people who worked at Marion's as attendants on a dark beach, from which fire-laden ships would carry dead warriors out to sea. So she said, "Viking burials? Much more splendid than the oven."

"Well, fire is fire, whatever place it's in. But that must have been a noble ritual."

Alice came into the room at that moment. "Ritual?" she asked.

"What now Lalla? Last time it was ghost stories."

"I have been diverted," Lalla said. "I came to tell you that Tom's arriving tomorrow, and that we're going to Italy next week."

"How lovely for you. It's time you had a holiday, anyway. Will you be able to bring Tom round to dinner one evening before you go?"

"I'd love to. May I wait till I find out what his plans are - if any?"

"Of course. And your own plans?"

"Well, I was supposed to stay at Marion's for two months, wasn't I? Now Matron wants me to stay on, and I thought that, if I didn't live in, but came for three days a week, anyway till Christmas, it would suit us all."

"You've made living there possible for Stella," Francis said. "It's made all the difference to her."

"She's made all the difference to me, too. I've told her about Italy, of course, but not about being a part-time person when I come back. I wanted to ask you if you'd tell her about that. I'm shirking, I know."

"As it's because of Tom, she'll understand very well. But I think that she'd much rather you told her yourself."

"I suppose so. You said that old age is about courage. Mine flags a bit. I have so much in the world, and a future that I feel is wonderful, and hope, I suppose. So that when I have to - want to - do things in my own favour I feel like the rich robbing the poor."

"They've all been young with futures, too - once. And I don't think that anyone would grudge your putting your own life first, though of course they may grumble a bit when it happens."

"You're right, of course," Lalla said. "I suppose that I'm so excited about seeing Tom again that I don't want to dilute pleasure. Again, having so much and hating taking away anything from anybody."

"Now you're almost treating Stella as if she was someone who must be protected from reality, and that is taking away from her."

Lalla said, "I see I can't get out of it. Thank you for reminding me."

"One of us will go round to see her tomorrow Lalla, and try to cushion the blow."

"She'll still be there when you get back, but I'm sorry that you'll miss her Prom."

"I'm sorry, in a way, but I know so little about music I'd probably say all the wrong things. Specially because I do admire her, and I might find her music much too difficult. And Tom's hopeless, he doesn't like anything he's heard written after - oh, I suppose the Thirties."

"I have felt like that, myself," Francis said, "I'm getting a bit more adventurous now."

"And, in any case we'll be there, so you will get a good first-hand report when you come home."

Lalla left, and Alice turned to Francis.

"I wonder why I said 'home'? Where is her home? Not at Marion's."

"Nowhere at present, just in the present, I suppose."

"Or wherever Tom is?"

"Let's wait till we know him to think about that."

Chapter 3

Francis woke before Alice. It was early, not quite six, he saw as he turned to the bedside clock. Alice had cocooned herself in rather more than her share of the duvet and was deeply asleep, her face buried in the pillow. Francis lay still, making the dream into words in case the visual memory should fade, even if the strong emotional impact lasted beyond the picture, still clear to him. He extricated himself gently and quietly from his side of their bed and went downstairs, switched on the kettle and then started to write.

The extraordinary thing about the dream was its briefness, 'this is how it will be, what you will find', and the fact that it should have been frightening, for the sky was dark, with some brilliantly blue-lit clouds, as if he'd seen them in the illumination of lightning. Yes, and there was lightning. He had stood on stony, boulder-scattered earth, and not far away a range of cliffs that were partly walls and towers, unlit, but he was sure they were not deserted. A place to which he must find his way? An assurance that such a place must exist? A treasure house? A terrible journey to achieve something unknown? He did not know, but the amazing thing had been the elation that this landscape had generated. Everything was on a vast scale, but it was excitement at its beauty that surprised him, and the loneliness of his presence there that had been not sad at all, but marvellous in the security of a loneliness he had never experienced in life, a serene moment from which he had woken.

It seemed strange to Francis that solitude should have been sensed as completion, it was so unlike his real, his dimensional, daylight feelings. If it became a poem, as two other of his dreams had done, it would surprise Alice as much as it had surprised him, for though both had their moments of solitude these times related to their return to each other.

The kettle boiled. Francis had written very few words in his notebook, but enough to freeze something of the dream for future use. He made tea, then realised that it was too early to wake Alice; he settled down in the kitchen, thinking about solitudes while he drank cup after cup of tea. The thoughts spun round Stella, about her work, her life, restricted as it had become by physical limitation, frustrated because imagination still ran so far ahead of performance, and her search for means to use that crippled right hand to catch the sounds she heard. That musical composition is mysterious to non-musicians must be obvious, but Francis could, to a certain extent, understand the amazing transference from initial ideas - the données of which she spoke - to their capture in notation. These had, again, to be translated into the separate strands of each instrumental voice, a labour far more complicated than his own work with words.

Very soon after breakfast when Francis had gone back to work and Alice was still reading "The Times", the front door bell rang. Alice put down the paper and went to the door expecting to see the milkman with a bill. But to her surprise it was Maria. Maria pale and looking, Alice thought at a first glance, frightened.

"Come in" she said, then "What's happened?" "Charles" said Maria. "Ill?" The idea of an accident, car, train, plane, rushed through Alice's mind as well as a picture of strokes, heart attacks, but before reason could persuade her that had this been the trouble, Maria would have telephoned to summon her, Maria said as Alice shut the door, "He's left." "Left?" Alice was still faintly unfocussed. "Left?" Then the situation became clear. "Come into the sitting room." Her first instinct was to gain time by offering coffee, but she suppressed it. Maria sank down on the sofa, and said, "I had no idea that it would feel like this." "When?" asked Alice, meaning, of course, when, where, how and why, and with whom?

'When' was the right word, for it unlocked Maria's words. "It's that ruddy little bitch of Stella's. You know that we saw her a good deal when we were in Sydney? I told you, of course I did, because you were talking about Stella, who is unutterably right to have nothing to do with her. I suppose that I've been idiotic too, I don't know how it was, because Charles and I have been together so long, it seemed as if we'd always be together, but now I look back, I can see things I never noticed, but I must have noticed them or I wouldn't remember them now..." The first torrent of words abated suddenly and she lit a cigarette. "He had to go back to Sydney to tidy up some ends of business, it was something to do with one of the wine companies. He had fingers in a lot of pies, and you know he's got a magic touch. Well, it was for a week or so, and I wasn't going, it's a ghastly flight, and so expensive. He said it was all too delicate for doing by post or telephone. This, Alice, is where there should be hollow laughter, so that he *must* go, and it seemed perfectly normal, and I never thought a thing about it, except that he wouldn't be here for a dinner party we'd been rather looking forward to at Mado and Everard's. But - what of that? Then this morning, this." She pulled an air letter out of her pocket and held it out to Alice.

Alice looked at her, at the letter, and again at Maria. "Would you mind reading it?" Maria asked. "I think that it would feel more real if you had seen it too. Just now I'm the only person who has seen it, I suppose, and it doesn't seem possible or real or bearable". She leant forward for Alice to take it and burst into tears.

Alice took it and put it down and got up and crossed to sit beside Maria on the sofa. She put her arm round her shoulders and hugged her.

"Oh Alice, I feel so primitively deserted," she said. "I don't know if I'm mortally wounded or only furious... Charles, of all people, and Désirée." She giggled, half crying, "Désirée, bloody Désirée of all people..."

"You said that you'd come to the conclusion that she was rather awful last time you spoke of her."

"Yes, I remember, and right I was. She's not good enough for Charles," she said defensively.

"Do you really want me to read his letter?"

"Yes I do."

"All right then." Alice picked it up, and still sitting next to Maria she started to read, then she said, "Damn. I'll have to get my glasses." She went to fetch them from on the kitchen table where they lay on the still opened paper. While she was there she also put on the kettle.

It was a short letter, full of something Alice couldn't place at first. Then it became clear to her that Charles liked Australia and saw himself as someone who had found his place there and that he realised that Maria hadn't liked it, never would fit in. Their years together had been so eventful, moving from new thing to new venture, from place to place, from moment to moment in an easily linked partnership that he had suddenly found inadequate. She began to see that Maria had probably half-known this for a much longer time but because everything worked pretty well for them she had had no reason or wish for the pattern to change. It was certainly an epitaph.

"Well," she said, giving it back. "It must have been dreadful for him to have to write it." Maria had mopped up her tears and lit another cigarette.

"Yes, I'll give him that. It's honest, but it's awful to discover how little I must have meant to him, and for years, I suppose."

"Did you have any idea...?"

"Well, in a sort of way. I mean I did assume that he had minor adventures when he went off on business trips. But we seemed to be so much a part of each other's necessities, he talked about all he was doing, so I didn't even bother, probably I didn't mind. You know I've been thinking, in a very drowning-man-seeing-life-pass way, since this came. It's extraordinary how much remembering one can get through between eight and ten, and how much emotion. Oh God Alice, I never thought my husband would just leave me after twenty years."

Alice was shocked too. She realised that she'd never questioned the solidity of Maria and Charles's marriage. "Twenty years, well I suppose it must be. You were married for about four years before we were."

"Yes and you had that miserable affair with - what was his name? And then we were so pleased about Francis." For a moment their young lives were present to them both. "How long ago everything is beginning to be," Alice said.

"It shows when the present cracks, one doesn't notice otherwise." Maria seemed to have learnt a lot of things that morning.

"I'd not thought of that. You mean we've all been living in a continuous present, and it's only when there's a sort of volcanic shift that one notices it's all divisible into chapters?"

"Yes, I think that's what I mean. There was life with Charles since we married, and now that's got finis written below the last paragraph."

"Do you feel it is final, Maria? Don't you think that this is - what did you call it? - a minor adventure?"

"I don't know. You see, if they existed, and I'm guessing now, they weren't spoken of. I assumed, from one trifle and another, and what people say, in a hinting kind of way, nothing explicit. I never took any notice" She paused. "But this, well, you saw the letter, it's not only leaving me, it's a new beginning for him."

"That's one of the strange things, people thinking that they can have that sort of new beginning; how can one without having all the past as ballast, I wonder?"

"It's so devaluing." Maria started to cry again.

"Well, he's the one who's devalued," Alice said sharply, "not you."

"No, I feel devalued, so I must be, that horrible Désirée - how could he? How could he?"

"She probably gazes at him and tells him he's wonderful all the time."

Maria stopped crying and looked at Alice. And then started to laugh. "Oh Alice, she looks like an emu."

"What do you mean? I thought that they have red eyes and shaggy feathers and black legs." Then the thought of a devoted emu gazing at Charles and telling him how wonderful he was made Alice laugh. They sat on the sofa together, completely helpless and shaking, Maria giving an occasional sob that turned into a hiccough, and then laughing again.

Francis came in, starting to ask if he had smelt coffee, which he hadn't. He stood, astonished, in the doorway.

"What on earth?" he began. Maria, suddenly calm, said, "Charles has left me, and it's Stella's daughter and Alice says she's like an emu."

Alice was about to contradict, but saw that this wouldn't help. "Well, the emu part isn't important, but Charles has gone back to Australia, and Maria thought that it was for a short business trip, but he's written to say that he's staying there, and that he's with Stella's daughter. The letter only came this morning."

"Oh my dear," said Francis, he sat on the arm of the sofa by Maria and put his arm round her shoulder. Maria lent down her head on his knee and started to cry properly.

Alice got up and went to the kitchen to make coffee, leaving Maria to have her cry in Francis's comforting presence.

She wondered then about practicalities. She'd never known whether Maria had any money of her own, or if Charles had been the well-off one. Or, indeed, what their financial situation might be. Maria had always looked rather better dressed than most people, but that was partly an innate elegance, a sense of what was right for her, a talent Alice admired and enjoyed. In fact, as she put cups on a tray, Alice wondered why she'd ever supposed that they'd known each other well, though they had known each other for such a long time.

Francis let Maria cry, keeping his arm across her shoulder, and murmuring to her, rather in the tone of voice he used to the cats. It calmed her, and she sat up and opened her bag and started to dab at her face with powder and lipstick. "Crying does make one look a fright. I am so sorry."

"You never look a fright," he said, reassuringly. "This must have been a hell of a shock..."

"Yes, it was, and all I could think of was coming here. But now, now I don't think it was quite such a shock as it seemed at first, I've begun to think back, and there were all sorts of clues, but I didn't see them before."

"Did he ever talk of settling in Australia?"

"Oh yes, at one time he talked about it a great deal, but it sort of wore off, and he'd talk of settling in all sorts of places. But I never thought that he meant any of it seriously. He's not a settling sort of man." She stopped suddenly and said, "Of course, I suppose that I'm part of that. He likes change, and new people, but I thought that he liked me all the time."

"I'm sure he did," Francis had supposed this, but he'd never known Maria and Charles as well as Alice had when they were all young.

"What are you going to do about that letter?" he asked, as Alice brought in a tray with coffee things.

"I hadn't thought about doing anything. I suppose I'll have to write to him. How does one address a husband who's walked out?"

Neither Alice nor Francis answered for a moment. "Depends on what you are going to say in the rest of it," Francis suggested.

"Don't write today," was Alice's contribution. To each it seemed, the more they thought about it, a letter impossible to write.

Francis, more detached from the whole business than was Alice, whose early friendship with Maria had in this crisis superseded her more critical, more questioning feelings of the last few weeks, felt that a lot of emotional demands would follow this morning. He wanted to protect Alice though he clearly realised that this would be impossible unless he offered his own shoulder for Maria to lean on, a prospect by which he was slightly attracted, but of which he was already wary.

"Would you like to stay here?" Alice asked. "I could come back while you pack a bag." She realised that she was treating Maria as if her home had been burgled, almost offering to call the police. In fact she felt that she was behaving idiotically. It was a situation that she'd never met at first-hand before. It was like and unlike a death, but this willed leaving had a non-final aspect. There was Charles in Australia, not translated to some unknown place or lost in oblivion but, none the less, in another dimension. Subject for so much fiction, it was quite different when it happened to a friend; theory was unlike advice, and any advice seemed useless at that moment.

"I don't know yet," Maria said. "I really don't know. I'll have to do things at home. After all Charles would have been away this week, anyhow, and I'd got all sorts of things planned, so I suppose that I might as well do them."

Alice imagined cupboards and chests of drawers with all Charles's clothes still in them. Again, she'd had to do that sort of clearing up, long ago when her great-uncle had died, but she had no idea what would be proper now. Pack them for transport to Australia? Obviously no precipitate action could be taken in case it was all a short-term drama from which Charles would return to find that his expensive suits and lovely shirts had been disposed of, or were crated up and winging their way to the Antipodes. Her mind was running ahead in a cinematic way and she found herself providing dialogue for these improbable moments.

After another hour spent in desultory talk Maria went home alone.

"Come here if you feel low. Or telephone, please," Alice said, kissing her at the door.

She came back to Francis. "What, but what, should we do?"

"Let the dust settle," he suggested. "I don't know what those two feel about each other, whether Charles felt that she didn't need him, and he needs to be needed, or if he's really involved seriously with Désirée, or whether he's on to an interesting business in Australia. I feel that I've never known him at all, always as part of a couple. What about you?"

"I suppose," Alice said, thinking slowly, "I've known him more by hearsay than by knowing him. He's been reported, or he used to be, by Maria, and come to think of it, always in action. Not much, if at all, by what he said. He always talked about going to places, not about what he saw there."

"Maria always seemed to admire him."

"Oh yes, and she likes the going about. But she used to see things and she always had much more interesting friends, more her friends than his. Don't you remember?"

At that moment the telephone started to ring. Francis answered it.

"Stella. How are you? Did she? I'll tell her, she may be a bit late. We've had an unexpected visit from a friend. Yes, of course my dear."

"Stella says she was expecting you at eleven."

"My God. I quite forgot. I suppose I'd better go."

"Can you face it?"

"She won't know anything about all this, or do you suppose she's heard?"

"They don't write very often, so it's unlikely."

"I'll probably be there till their lunch, then I shan't do anything at all this afternoon. Other people's crises are exhausting." Alice sighed, as she picked up her bag and got out the keys of the car.

Stella was in her room. It had started to rain and the sky was dark with cloud. She had her reading lamp on and sat in a pool of light. The room smelt of roses. Someone had sent her a huge bunch of garden flowers, and they were on the table beside her.

"Alice - at last."

"Sorry I'm so late. We had an early and unexpected visitor and I couldn't get away." "So Francis said. People shouldn't drop in. Not that it's my business. But you shouldn't allow it. Guess what's happened though?" She pointed to an air-letter beside the flowers.

"Nothing awful I hope." Alice spoke lightly.

"Awful no, quite otherwise. That idiot daughter of mine has written the most euphoric bit of nonsense ever to be put on paper. Love she says, love - well I don't think she knows the meaning of the word, but look. You can read it if you can stand that sort of gush."

For the second time that morning Alice had an airmail letter thrust into her hand and, rather unwillingly, she read Désirée-Joanna's account of Charles.

They'd known each other for some years, they'd been attracted at once, Charles's wife was unsympathetic to him, didn't like Australia, didn't ... Alice found herself wanting to speak up for Maria as she read on about 'the real thing at last' and such clichés, but she decided not to involve any other strand of her life, at least for the moment.

"Well," she said, handing the letter back to Stella, "she sounds very pleased with herself, and him, and life."

"If he's fled from an un-understanding wife - and how many times have you heard that? - he'll stay in Australia and so will she, Stella said with grim satisfaction.

"All for her best, then." Alice spoke as if it were an epitaph for Charles.

"I suppose so." Stella shifted her weight, light though it was, as if sitting still was uncomfortable.

"Do you want me to bring you another cushion?"

"Oh my dear, I doubt if any cushion is going to be much use. I'm simply crumbling, probably my bones look as if they'd been in a tumulus for years."

All the same Alice did fetch a cushion from a pile on the bed. "Try this," she said, and slipped it behind Stella's thin shoulders.

"Yes, better. Thank you. What do you suppose the wife is like?"

"Quite unlike Joanna."

"Alice, you're hiding something from me."

Stella was very quick in her reactions when the subject was interesting.

"Yes I was." No help for it now. "I do know Charles and his wife. At one time we were all very close. Actually they were angels to us when we were getting married."

"And now?"

"They've been abroad for ages, and it had almost reached the Christmas-card-only stage. Then, just a few weeks ago, Maria turned up looking gorgeous. All golden brown and splendid and I was very glad to see her."

"And Charles?"

"Madly successful," she said. "But he did behave in a slightly objective way. Now I see that they must have lost touch with each other and been overwhelmed by too much of everything, or something like that. I've only seen him once, and briefly, since they came back."

"What a fool he must be to leave a friend of yours for Joanna."

"I don't know what she's like, of course. Maria can be a ball of fire when she gets going. She started Francis on his fortunes."

"Now I suppose," Stella looked at Alice shrewdly, "she'll be weeping on his bosom rather than on yours. This is just the sort of thing that happens. You'd better take him away for a holiday."

"Really Stella." Alice was surprised, amused and then quite fiercely annoyed. "Francis is perfectly capable of mopping up Maria's tears without messing up our lives."

"You're too nice, Alice, that's your trouble."

"Don't you think that you're under-rating Francis?"

"Well, he's a good poet, and that is something I'm sure about."

Stella was placating her with a real offering, for she was always truthful about those arts she valued, and their practitioners, no flattery at all. But Alice saw that this was a side issue at the moment. Stella had not withdrawn her warning.

Chapter 4

Lalla and Tom were on their way to dinner with the Dulacs. Tom was full of questions about the house. "You'll see for yourself," Lalla said, but he persisted. "It's not very big, in one of the turnings off Gloucester Avenue, near the canal. It's squarish, and there's what Alice calls a pretend garden in front, a little strip of rose bushes and things. There's a square hall, tiny too, with a long narrow looking-glass on the wall. I think there are three rooms on the ground floor because he has a room to work in, and there's a sitting room as well as the kitchen. And that has pictures in it, dark red walls; it's about the biggest room in the house, it's even got a sofa there, mostly for the cats, I think. The sitting room is all bookshelves, and lovely furniture, not much, but all walnut or rosewood. Sofas again. It's comfortable. Oh well, you'll see."

"What sort of pictures?"

"What I'd call modestly ancestral, eighteenth century pastels in oval frames, and the best kind of great-aunt watercolours. And there are lots of flowers."

Tom was amused by Lalla's description. "So I guess that it smells of ancestral beeswax?"

"She used to work in an antique shop, so I suppose that is what it smells of. I couldn't place it. Oh yes, and he smokes rather a lot, and she has some delicious scent."

"Better and better."

"They sit in the garden a lot. It's a tangly little garden at the back of the house. I think that they think that they like gardening, but they really like sitting in it with their cats. Perhaps they do do something, sometimes, as there are lots of flowers. But it isn't big. Oh yes, and they have a maytree which one of their cats sits in a great deal."

"It sounds too good to be true. I do hope that I shall like them as you like them so much."

"Oh you will, you will," Lalla promised.

As it was hot weather still, Alice had made a rather frivolous meal, ending deliciously with summer pudding. They sat in the garden afterwards drinking coffee and Armagnac, while Tom talked about America.

"Quite a different sort of age there," he said, "the very lively elderly women. They seem to have inexhaustible energy, as if they were burning up left over fuel that their earlier years had not touched."

"Like the fall colours?" Francis suggested.

"Do you remember that man, who was it, Tom? Who said at some party 'Thank God the grass doesn't go red, too'." Lalla asked and answered her own question.

"Oh yes, it was one of the Professors who had hated the States."

"You can always find things to dislike anywhere," Tom said. "I enjoyed Granny's friends for a short time. I couldn't have stood them for too long."

"It's an odd contrast, those who let go, and those who cram in all they can," Lalla said. "It's observable all the time."

"How does your ghost-story teller fit in?" Francis asked.

"He's one of the third kind, I think," Tom said. "He's probably always been an observer and commentator. He'd see no point in cramming-in, and he'll not let go, just ripen gently till he falls."

"I suppose that's why we like him so much." Lalla turned to Francis. "He doesn't make either of us feel that he's in a category. Your third section," she accused Tom, "is his alone, so far."

"Your work, and yours," Alice smiled at Francis, "are running parallel in a sort of way, aren't they?"

"Is it talkable about?" Tom asked. He'd carefully refrained from saying anything about Francis's poems though he'd wanted to, but it seemed not to be the right moment, too soon he thought.

"Not really. But I think it's getting too big and too long, and what started with Stella is becoming almost a rag-bag of odds and ends, and I'm trying to find what I can make out of them."

"So, what you are all exploring is some sort of unknown land?" As Alice spoke she had a picture in her thoughts of so many people she had known, ageing: ageing hands, and thin hair and bent shoulders, and she still named it courage.

"It's one we're all likely to have to explore," said Tom cheerfully. It was still distant enough for him and for Lalla to feel objective about, and the talk turned easily to other things, particularly to the coming holiday.

After they'd left Alice said to Francis that perhaps they should think of a holiday too.

"It's infectious talk, isn't it?" he answered. "Where do you think we should go?"

"Such a lot of wheres." Alice was drying the glasses. Francis was doing the washing-up. "It's the when, you know, that I'm thinking of."

"I think this old age thing will be finished soon."

"In spite of what you told Tom?"

"Well, yes. It's strange how just saying something that I thought approximately true when I said it, suddenly crystallized what I must do next."

"No wonder you were rather vague over the Armagnac." Alice had sometimes described herself as 'a buffer state', a term she remembered with amusement from otherwise forgotten history lessons, the edicts and the treaties of remote wars, unreal in their implications. She had much preferred literature, and the only wars she had taken seriously were those recorded by Shakespeare or by Wilfred Owen.

"Did I leave too much to you?" he asked, handing her the last batch of spoons to dry.

"No, no, they were so easy, and had plenty to say. I doubt if they noticed that you were absent."

He said, as he took off the apron, "So the when is settled then - after Stella's Prom. Where?" They spent another hour dawdling to bed over that question.

Tom and Lalla were also talking about the evening as they walked back to Marion's. Tom had liked both Alice and Francis. He said, "He's rather a silent creature."

"Great thoughts?"

"Perhaps. They're much more comfortable to be with than the Americans I've been experiencing."

"You must not grumble about all the comforts you've been enjoying and you know you did enjoy yourself."

"Except for missing you, Lalla. Only two more days and then Italy. I wish you hadn't got to go back to Marion's tonight."

"So do I, oh dear, so do I. But you will come to tea tomorrow, won't you, and meet Dame Stella?"

"I will, I will. I want to see this extraordinary creature. Is she a genius, is she, Lalla? It's rather exciting to meet an aged genius when you consider all our others."

They walked more and more slowly as they got nearer, and then stayed strolling in the garden for another half hour. Lalla reminded him that she had to be on duty at eight and they parted at last, reluctantly and lovingly.

"Tomorrow and Friday," said Tom. "And then . . . "

"Today and Friday," said Lalla as she unlocked the door.

When Tom went round to Marion's the next day at a quarter to four, Lalla met him at the door. First she took him to Matron's office, and introduced him. His eye was quick to register details, as it had been at the Dulacs the night before, following Lalla's account of their house and adding extra observations with interest.

Mrs. Miles had a pleasant room, which Tom had expected to find something like a headmistress's study in a girls' school, though as he'd never been inside such a room the expectation was entirely fictional. The window sill was filled with plants, all sorts of geraniums, some with velvety leaves, the green darkened by rings of deeper colours, tiny rosy and coral flowers in little spikes, some palest pink, some crimson, one white as the linen curtains. The room was pale green, and amazingly tidy, and Mrs. Miles herself a small, pretty woman rather more gentle-looking than he'd imagined she would be from Lalla's amused and admiring description of the way she handled her difficult charges.

"I'm so glad you've found time to visit Dame Stella. Lalla's been her mainstay here, and I don't know that she'll forgive you for borrowing her, and borrowing is the only word she'll allow. But I expect you can persuade her that it's a good idea."

She liked the look of him. Quite a lot taller than Lalla, and much taller than herself, she looked up into a square face, broad forehead, blue eyes that looked bluer because he was so sunburned, and hair dark brown, almost curly. A good face, she decided, open, friendly. Lalla had no photographs in her room, so she'd not had any idea; in fact she'd expected much more earnestness, glasses, a picture invented round the words 'research project', which had alarmed her when the idea of Lalla coming to work at Marion's had first been discussed.

"When we come back from Italy, may I come to see you?" he asked. "I've heard so much about this place from Lalla, and it sounds to me as if it's all amazingly right. As if you'd found some way of making things work, and letting people enjoy themselves."

She was pleased by this.

"Yes, I should like that, and yes, we have, to some extent. The people here are a very small minority though, and they are cushioned. It's not too hard to manage when we can offer so much. I expect you've seen a good deal of different ways of living through the last part of life? As I have," she added, making common ground with him. "But now you must go up to Dame Stella and then you can all have tea in her room. Special treat, Lalla. The tray's in the pantry. She's developed a great liking for Jaffa cakes, so that is what you will have."

Tom laughed. "Lalla's always had a great liking for Jaffa cakes," he said.

"This is Tom, Dame Stella, Tom Mayfield." Stella looked fragile but spectacular with her emerald cloak wrapped round her and draped over a footstool. A queen in exile Tom decided romantically, and with sudden inspiration he almost knelt to kiss her hand.

She beamed at him. "Sit down here," she said, pointing at a chair close to her own, "and talk about America to me."

"My grand-mother is American," he began, "so I'm a quarter American myself. So I've been over there often." He stopped and then said as an aside, "She pays my fare."

Stella laughed. "That's lucky for you." Then, more seriously, "What do you do while you're there?"

"Sometimes I do some work. This time I did. It was fun, too, because I did a lot of sailing, and that is one of the things Lalla hates, so I didn't feel that I was defrauding her of a pleasure."

"Bad sailor," Lalla corroborated. "I can't bear the sea unless I'm on a beach, then I love it."

"Tell me about the work part. It's always more interesting."

"There's a family business. I'm not much involved, but I keep in touch, in case. And I talked with Granny's friends. They're mostly retired and well heeled, and I believe they think themselves immortal; they're barricaded from everything."

"Barricaded?"

"Yes, Dame Stella. There are such rigid patterns, and inside those they live. Time for breakfast, coffee time, hairdresser time or massage time, drinks time, lunch time, rest hour, tea time, bridge time - and after all that, bed time; it's a marvellous cage."

"And the others?"

"Well, I got to know some quite different people, the ones who hang about. And they're quite the opposite because they have nothing to do at all, so they live in space and expect nothing. Nothing but weather, and an odd cigarette. But they had pasts which they spoke of as if they were stories they'd heard. Not as if they regretted busy times or dangerous times. Sit and sketch, and they'll come and look over my shoulder and they talk, sometimes as if they forget I can hear as well as draw."

"Tell me, then," Stella said. "What are you doing, you two? Recording what a lot of different old people are like? Alice has talked to me about you both. Or are you trying to draw conclusions about old age?"

"It started as being about old age and what old people need, rather social awareness, like Mayhew, we hoped, at the beginning. But now it's got rather too big for us. And we've been talking about what we should do with all our material."

"The odd thing is," Lalla said, "that the stuff we've actually recorded, and there's quite a lot, comes out very like Mayhew. Just not quite such bad circumstances, as the mudlarks, for instance."

"But," Tom broke in, "we don't know if it will be any use at all."

"I think it's been of use to me," Lalla said. "And I've learned a lot here, but it's all been practical, about the practical things that are needed, and perhaps why."

Stella said, "Matron was much jollier after the row last week. I think that my behaving badly cheered everyone up. It wasn't what I intended, but they're all so tame. I felt that I should behave badly more often."

"If you do it with conviction," Lalla said, "not just for fun."

"Easy enough I should think," Tom said. "I behaved badly once or twice this summer, and I know just what you mean. Once you've started you can't stop."

"You too?"

"Oh yes. They were being impossible about, well, they kept on being impossible about everything: the servants, homosexuals, blacks, Catholics, Jews, taxes. Nothing was right, and there they were in blue-haired comfort."

"Gin-sodden cockatrices", Stella contributed, and looked Lalla straight in the eye.

"It's whisky here, isn't it?" Lalla answered back briskly.

Tom said he thought it was a good thing that he was taking Lalla away before she was corrupted.

"But you'll bring her back?"

"Of course, but you won't be here much longer. Won't you be going back to your flat?"

"I wonder, sometimes, if I'll be able to manage alone. It's going to be a problem, and I can't think how I can have anyone living in with a spare room the size of a parrot cage."

This was the first time she'd confessed to worrying about a problem that everyone who thought of her future had been discussing with apprehension.

"Don't leave while we're away," Lalla said.

"Perhaps Tom will come and live with me. I'd much rather have a man to live with."

"I'd be honoured." Tom stood up, thinking he'd better cut the conversation short before it turned into a plan.

He kissed her hand again, before he picked up the tea tray to carry it away. "Thank you for letting me come to see you," he said.

"I'll be back in a minute". Lalla followed him out, and down the stairs.

"And I can just see that happening." She led him into the kitchen and unloaded the tea things. "You must be careful how you respond to offers."

"It's extraordinary how fascinating she is. I can't think why, when you consider everything against it but something works still; charm?"

"Yours or hers?" Lalla was not quite sure of the answer herself.

"Both", said Tom, kissing Lalla, who then let him out of the front door, and they both said, as if it were a promise, "Tomorrow."

Maria's idea for a programme about Stella had become something so different in Francis's mind that he was relieved when he was asked to take part in a television interview about the work that Stella had been commissioned to write for the Proms. He supposed that Maria would be glad, now, not to undertake anything remotely connected with Charles's defection, and he could keep his old-age sequence to himself for the time being, for it had become the central occupation of his thoughts. Francis talked to Stella about what she wanted to say about the work so that he could ask her the proper questions. He realised, with pleasure, that it was she who had asked for him to take part in the interview because she had enjoyed setting his poems. This time words had no part in her piece, for it was a series of episodes, each one for a solo instrument, characters stepping out of the ensemble to make a separate statement, she explained. He was glad that he would not be alone in interviewing her for he felt that he would be out of his depth, musically, though he understood the end rather better than he grasped the technicalities of the means.

"But it will be comforting to have him there," Stella said to Alice - "being away from my own life as I am. It would be different if I could have done the interview at home - studios are so impersonal and so airless."

Of course, when the day for the interview came her nerves were calmed at once. She was professional and collected as well as excited. The make-up girl had been deft and flattering, a touch on the eyelids, a feathering of colour, a delicate lightening of powder, and, suddenly she felt like a beauty. The talk with one of the most musical and talented of the BBC music staff and with Francis flowed in easy confidence, and no-one became too technical. Stella spoke easily of the excitement of writing for the spare groups of instruments she liked to use and for the human voice. She was steered tactfully away from the stuff she had written in her earlier days for blue films, which she had been discussing before the interview started, being a little too funny and a lot too explicit for the camera man's comfort as he and the lighting crew prepared for work.

Afterwards they took her out to lunch and she continued with her tales of the past, as Francis told Alice: "I knew some of it, but when she gets going it's amazing and embroidered - and quite a lot true I should think - she must have been terrifying to her lovers, she needs a major Elizabethan to match her, and from all I know none of them were up to snuff, and she must have known it all the time."

"So it's no wonder that she abandoned them, then."

Alice was glad that Stella was so much older than Francis, and said so, laughing.

"And so am I," he answered. "Thankful - for if I'd been a contemporary of hers - you'd have been far too young for me."

"So time would have made us miss each other and we should never have known."

"Anyway," Francis said, "all her lovers were musicians, so I wouldn't have stood a chance."

Back at Marion's the elation ebbed away; Stella lay on her bed, tired to the bone and wondering if she'd made a fool of herself, said too much, said too little. The morning's work took on a dream perspective. She telephoned Alice.

"Did he say I was all right?" she asked. "Oh yes, brilliant, he said, and you do all seem to have had a good time after as well. Francis came reeling in at tea time, full of it all, and he said that you looked wonderful."

"Oh good. Yes, I could talk about everything, after it was over. That Patrick chap was easy, I think he asked the right questions. Was Francis really pleased?"

"Stella - I can't bear having to wait to see the programme. It sounds terrific."

"Well, I hope so. I feel flattered by it all."

"Relax, relax, you've done a good day's work."

"The trouble is that I want to do a good day's real work, and I can't. Talking about it isn't anything much."

"The excitement's wearing off, and that's a dreadful feeling." Alice sympathised, she knew all about that when certainty turns to doubt, doubt to despair, and the only cure is the discipline of the next stage, whatever that may be, correction, re-writing, turning to something else. She'd lived with it since marriage.

"I shan't want any supper tonight," Stella went on. "Television, I think. Any old thing, a Western would be best, and some whisky."

"That sounds a good plan. Are you still in your finery?"

"No, dressing gown. It's bliss to have it over."

She went on talking, and Alice listened, with half her attention, thinking of how she could end the spate of talk without hurting Stella's feelings or casting her back into solitude.

Francis came into the room and took the telephone from her.

"Goodnight Stella, and thank you for everything," he said. "Love from us both."

He put the receiver down.

"You won't see it you know. They're showing it in the Prom interval."

"I forgot. And we'll be there. And she won't see it either."

"No, at least, we might get someone to video it for us, and see it later.

But you've probably heard it all before, anyway, and I heard it all this morning." He was glad that it was over.

"Now," he said. "Now I can get on with the proper job."

"How are you going to manage? I mean this Prom thing was fine, you say, but Maria's project?"

"I've got to talk to her about that, and soon." As he spoke, Francis felt relieved. He would have to talk to Maria, to tell her that he could not do it, because it had burst its bounds. Instead of a sort of half-hour life-study it was turning into a book. Changing from pictures of Stella as a young girl, with a fiddle under her arm going into the Academy, Stella at an early concert with other young players who had become successful, one even famous, and were by now, except to their contemporaries and near contemporaries, forgotten. Stella in Greece, Stella in Italy, even, he had been amused to discover, Stella in "Vogue". Stella in a tin hat as a firewatcher. That, with her reminiscence, had been a good idea for an interesting late-night programme, for a small audience. But, he was sure, someone else could, and would in time, undertake it. He had other ideas, so many, in fact, that he was beginning to have a far too large assembly of possibilities and he knew that he'd have to start the drudgery of getting them into shape. At moments he wished it was a block of marble or granite he had to deal with, letting out the creature he divined to be inside the stone, chipping away to explore and to discover what he wished to find.

Stella had said to him once that whenever she felt daunted by the expanse of manuscript paper, she cheered herself up by wondering what on earth it had felt like to stand in front of the empty canvas that would become 'The Night Watch'. He was in exactly that stage. So he said again, "Yes, I'll have to tell Maria I can't do anything about her little biography."

"It's possible, isn't it, that Maria will be absolutely off anything to do with Stella? She hasn't said anything about it - I mean your programme - since the Charles letter, has she?"

"No, nothing. I suppose that I had better confirm that she's off the idea."

"Take her out to lunch," said Alice. "She'd love to be taken out. It's a limbo patch in her life now."

As she said it she remembered Stella's warning, and hated herself for doing so.

Maria was restless, disorganised, angry and, to her surprise, lonely. She felt totally out of focus. So she started to think about Charles, all the things that she disliked about him, now apparent as cumulative tiresomeness. And yet they had not, she was sure, been enough for her to wish him out of her life. She realised that he certainly was out of her life, and for ever. Alice half-supposed, quite obviously, that he'd come back eventually, and that she had breathing space to decide if she wanted to resume their lives, or to make treaties. But though it was a sort of possibility she was clear enough in her mind that she would not want such a return. Then, she felt elated. "It's a sort of second chance," she thought, "a new chapter, a beginning, a gift, almost; all this time, a choice of where I go and what I do." She decided to go to see her solicitor, the bank manager, the house agents, a delicious flurry of occupations. But then came the creeping thought, "so I never loved him. I can't have done, if going house-hunting becomes such a possible alternative. Did I, did I love him? If not, what about all those tears?"

She went to find an old photograph album and turning over pages of her past she remembered happy days, pictures of them, newly together, sailing, on beaches, skiing, one of Charles sitting in the sunshine. And a heavy homesickness for the past overcame her, for days of brightness, of sunlight on water, sunlight on snow, for a companionship she remembered as she looked at a photograph of Charles with his hand on her shoulder, her face turned to him, his to her.

So it was true, she thought, it was true, we really were those people, and who are we now? The day dragged on and on, full of regrets and finalities.

So, when the telephone rang and Francis suggested the next day for a meeting, Maria was delighted to be asked out to lunch. She had wanted to see Francis more than anyone she knew. By now, so many friends or acquaintances that she and Charles had once had in London were almost strangers, none were intimates any more, she was realising sadly. It was clear to her that being on her own would mean having to make a different sort of life and she wondered how to set about it. Her house-hunting plans had gone cold on her anyway, and her sudden energy had ebbed away.

Francis took her to a restaurant in Camden Lock. The canal was busy, just beyond the window people were operating the lock gates, taking their boats up towards Regent's Park. Most of them had children and dogs on board and a lively dumb-show was there for their entertainment. The willow-reflecting water was changing, with cascades of silvery water, reflections of scarlet and green and yellow boats and anoraks. The dogs ran about excitedly, crossed the lock gates with perfect balance and appeared to be finding it all much more fun than the humans, turning handles and keeping a watch on what their children were doing, and getting their boats through the lock.

"Well," said Maria. "This is friendly of you, Francis."

"I wanted to see you." He was going to continue the sentence with 'about Stella', but as he spoke he realised that he had wanted to see her very much, Stella or no Stella.

"I wanted to see you." She echoed his words with much the same inflection. They stared at each other for a moment, then Francis said what he'd intended.

"About Stella..."

"Yes?"

"I can't do a programme about her. I think that interview will have to do."

"Yes."

"It's all changed now. I've started something else, and she'll come into it in some way or another, but it can't be just her."

"I'm relieved you know. I'd thought, when you were talking about her, that it would be a pair with your William - the long nights - and I think that I wanted to be involved with your work again. Now, with Charles going off with Stella's daughter, that's worn off. I don't want to have anything to do with that or with her."

"Of course. I expected you to say so."

"Yes, you would expect that. But then why should you? It has got de-personalised for you, I suppose."

"Oh Maria, I am sorry. That is exactly what had happened, and of course I guessed that you wouldn't want to be involved."

"I wouldn't have really. I was thinking of getting re-involved with your work, I suppose."

She repeated herself, and realised that she had done so.

He said nothing for a few minutes, looking at the water outside, and the busy movement beside it.

"I've been thinking about you too much for my own comfort, not enough for yours."

"Oh I'll withdraw," she said. "I'll leave you in your safety."

This was what he wanted to happen, but he knew that, at this time, when her life was in confusion, it would be almost impossible. Alice, he thought, would insist on seeing her, helping her, and - as she had done today - sending him off to comfort and protect and cheer.

Otherwise, he'd have to tell Alice that he didn't want to see Maria. And then he imagined she'd think him heartless, or worse, she'd see that he was becoming far too involved, and how would she react to that? All this flashed through his mind as he filled their glasses. Something to do with his hands, a trifling action staving off a decisive one.

"What are you thinking of doing?" he asked.

She caught his mood, guessed his thoughts.

"My choices are limited, aren't they? I suppose that I will try to find a job. I will move to a small flat. I will sit by the telephone in the evenings. Or will I fall in love, or shall I spend my time running round to see Alice in the hope of seeing you?"

She looked at him. "Worst of all, Francis, that makes it your choice, doesn't it?"

"You make it sound as if we have no choice."

"You have. I can go or stay."

"I can't offer you anything worth having. You need far more of someone's life. I haven't that to offer."

As they spoke, he found himself wondering to what sort of music this operatic duet should be set.

The waiter hovered. He was used to drama, to couples mutually absorbed, and so inconsequent about their food.

Francis was relieved to be able, for the moment, to break the tension.

"Maria?"

She picked up the menu, and without paying it attention, said,

"Oh - melon."

"And then?"

"Some fish I think."

"Melon and then salmon," Francis turned to the waiter, "for two."

The waiter teased them with questions about vegetables or salad, new potatoes? It seemed to take a long time. Eventually he finished writing down their order.

"It's all right. It's just bloody loneliness, and I like you more than anyone I know. I probably shouldn't for long. But, if you were available, and I know you aren't, how lovely that would be." She paused. "I suppose I need someone to restore my self-esteem."

"I wish we weren't in this bloody restaurant."

Francis leant across the table and took her hand. Of course, when they'd finished lunch, talking normally again, he walked her home, and of course he went in with her, and equally of course, with sudden, and to himself surprising certainty, they made love. She was the first person with whom he had had that experience since marriage. To his amazement, when it was over, he found that he had forgotten Alice entirely and all the reservations, all the thoughts of complications had melted away in a blaze of pleasure and refreshment. It had been so natural, that to his surprise he did not feel guilty or unhappy or worried about what he should say or do when he went home.

Maria almost asked Francis if he would tell Alice what had happened. He had dressed, and he stood by the window looking into the branches of the lime tree outside. Then he turned, and went to sit on the bed beside her. She knew, not only that he would never speak of what had happened, but that it would never happen again. It was something absolutely complete, and completed between them. She stretched out her arms and he bent to kiss her.

"I must go."

"Yes. I know."

"Thank you, thank you, Beauty."

"Francis?"

"All is well, my dear."

"And for me. Extraordinary but true. I think that I can still come to see you both."

"But of course."

They were surprised by the simplicity of the moment. It wasn't at all what Francis would have expected of himself had he imagined himself becoming someone's lover, while Maria realised that she had been restored to what she might have called human status again. It all seemed so natural and so familiar that nothing untoward in the future could spoil, change or corrupt its wholeness.

He went away, and she lay on her bed till the afternoon became evening.

On his way home Francis decided to go into the public library, to look up a reference that had been eluding him. He knew quite well that he was playing for time, that he needed to make a space between Maria and Alice, and this seemed geographically sensible, so he joined a small queue by the stop from which the 74 bus started. He planned to take the longest way there, to go a short way by bus, then walk up by Regent's Park Road, and along to Swiss Cottage, wasting time, making time, almost passing his door, but avoiding it. There were two empty buses standing there, and when a third one drew up behind them and the driver and conductor left, the waiting would-be passengers started to grumble. There were two women with trolley baskets full of vegetables, a girl with two children, both sticky from the fruit lollies they were finishing, a couple who, in spite of the sultry weather, were wearing thick cardigans and muttering to each other about some grievance, a young man with spiky green hair, and last in the row an elderly man who spoke immediately to Francis.

"None of this lot'll be going next," he said.

"No?"

"Not likely. It'll be a Roehampton one, you'll see."

"Oh?"

"I know them, I know their habits, see? I spend my time on the buses." Francis wondered if he'd passed this information on to the others before his own arrival. Obviously he had.

"People aren't interested, not really. But I know the buses."

"You travel often, then?" Francis began to be interested.

"Since the bus pass, you might say. Well, really since the wife passed on. You see she had no time for going out, so she said, though she'd have liked it if she'd tried, but she wouldn't."

So there were options. Should he commiserate on the wife's lack of enterprise, or on her passing on, Francis wondered, but instead he asked, "Always the 74?"

"Oh no, all of them. Mostly going south. Out all day, now, don't care for the digs. She can't cook a decent meal. Not that she isn't kindly, she is, but it's all foreign food. So I go to caffs for dinner. Nice woman down in Putney, good grub. Cheap too." He turned to Francis confidentially. "Two helpings of steak and kidney, or a bit of pie and vegetables, then apple tart, or pudding, and cups of tea, as many as you want. And all that for two pounds, and a nice clean place."

"Good value," said Francis.

"Mind you, I go all over. Get to know London. Amazing places you see everywhere, all the sights."

"Do you - well, get off and look at - museums?"

"No. Oh no, not much interested in things indoors, but I like best crossing the river. I know all the bridges, like looking at the river, up and down, best at high tide of course. I like it at night too, all them lights reflected, but I'm not often out late, have to get back before too late, so I save the dark for a treat sometimes. It's not like the old days though, is it? I liked the trams best. They made a friendly sound they did, but no passes. In them days we all had to pay."

"How many bridges are there?" Francis was not sure.

"Well, Tower Bridge of course, and then London Bridge, and the railway bridge to Cannon Street, Southwark Bridge, Blackfriars, Waterloo, Hungerford, Westminster, Lambeth, Vauxhall, Chelsea, Albert, Battersea, Wandsworth, Putney, Hammersmith, Chiswick and Kew, Twickenham, Richmond, Hampton Court - I know them all." It sounded like a litany. He was delighted to have a listener. No one else in the queue was attending to him.

"Some buses are better than others. I like the 38 in winter, nice warm bus, and you can get 36 down to Dulwich, all along by the cemetery it's very pretty, and up to Edmonton way; down the Old Kent Road, that's the 53 to Plumstead marshes, by Greenwich Park and Blackheath, you know."

"Goodness," said Francis, "I suppose you can go for miles in all directions."

"Oh yes. I did go over the Woolwich ferry once, but I didn't stay over, came back without getting off. People don't travel much, do they? Just their usual, never think to look beyond their noses, do they?"

He gave a disparaging look at the queue, which was now rather longer. Someone ahead of them sighted another bus, and everyone moved a few paces forward, looking ready to leave.

"That'll be it, you'll see. That'll be the one."

When the bus pulled in, he turned to Francis, "I go on top, see the world better that way." And small, neat and brisk as a sailor leaping into the rigging of a sailing ship, he was off, ahead of the basket ladies, beating even the sticky children to the upper deck. Francis, having so short a way to go, stayed downstairs; already there was a layer of other experience between Maria's room and his return home.

When, an hour later, he went into the house he found Alice sitting at the kitchen table, with a pile of sewing on one side of her, and tea things on the other. She was not sewing, but reading.

"Goodness, I lost count of time," she said.

"Busy day?" he asked.

"No, and yes. All the usual things, too much telephone. Stella is in a flap about Thursday. She thinks we'd better get a car for the rehearsal as well as for the concert."

"Well, why not?"

"Oh yes, I agreed. Parking's always difficult. Then I'd just discovered how to do a fiddly job, putting new shoulder straps on a petticoat"- Alice liked old-fashioned words - "one of those gadgetty little arrangements so that you shorten them, you know, that lacey white one, and she rang again, so I left the sewing here, and when I came back those foul cats were playing with it, and they'd pulled the ribbon out, and lost the little metal bit, and I couldn't remember how it went." She laughed at herself. "So it was all a time-consuming nonsense."

"You never were any use at gadgets," he said, picking up the lacey trifle, "but that looks all right to me."

"It is all right," Alice proclaimed, "though I felt as if I'd invented the steam engine by the time I got it right."

"And the cats let you?"

Alice said that by the time they'd created confusion they were bored and had gone out.

"And Maria?" she asked.

"You were right, she liked being taken out. She's adrift at the moment, of course. But not - " not what, he wondered. Miserable? Angry? "in disarray," he said. Then he thought how quickly his mind had worked playing with the words.

"I went on to the Library. And Alice, such an odd and enterprising man in the bus queue." He told her of his encounter, and to his amazement the evening settled into an accustomed pattern. He did want, he found he wanted very badly, to ring Maria, but there was no moment when it would have been possible to do so. He was particularly nice to the cats; their devilish work with Alice's ribbons had been, for him, providentially diverting.

Chapter 5

Two days later Francis and Alice went to Marion's. Stella's piece was to be rehearsed after the break, so they had decided to take her to the Albert Hall by eleven. She was nervous, though she said that the conductor, Giles Farnaby, who neither of them had met, had been most helpful. He'd been to see her several times, to discuss the score, and to tell her about the earlier rehearsals he had had.

"It's maddening beyond belief, being so wobbly," she said.

"Much less than you were," said Alice. "You look interestingly fragile, not wobbly, anyway."

They didn't talk as the comfortable and large car they had hired was driven through the streets towards the park. It was a rainy morning, but warm with a pearly, misty greyness. Stella looked out of the window, absorbed by the strangeness and pleasure of the scenes she had not had any chance of observing for months. The park was extraordinarily green, the grass had not bleached to the usual late-summer brown, for there had been many rainy nights. The trees were darkly dripping, heavy with the weight of rainwet leaves.

She turned to Alice. "It's quite extraordinarily beautiful," she said. "I'd forgotten how magical it can look. Those willows by the Serpentine - the variation of shape and colour. It's almost worth being in exile to see everything again after so long."

The lights changed colour, the car slipped down Exhibition Road, then up the slope past the red-brick blocks of flats, and to the door marked 'Artists' Entrance'. The orchestra's van was parked beside the building.

Francis and the driver helped Stella out. She stood for a moment looking about. The rain had stopped.

"God Almighty, they've cleaned the College of Organists' building. What a riotous bit of architecture it is."

"Very cheering after all the grey concrete we go in for nowadays, in my view," said Alice.

By this time the doorman had come down to the pavement and greeted Stella.

"Good to see you here again," he said, and he helped her up the steps. Francis followed, carrying her score; Alice followed him thinking how amazingly Stella collected a retinue, or made it seem as if she and Francis and the doorkeeper were a supporting cast. Soon they'd moved down to the front row of the stalls in the block near the orchestra, and Giles had come to greet her. She introduced Alice and Francis, "My friends the Dulacs," and abandoning them, she sat bent over her score which Francis had put on the ledge in front of her.

"There's that place, here, four bars after figure 9," he said, "the flute's entry..." They were deep in technicalities till a girl came through the door onto the stage with a tray of plastic coffee mugs.

"You'll have some too, won't you?" Giles said to Alice. "Thank you, Thisbe." Thisbe, red-haired and freckled, put the tray on the steps beside them, and hung about, till Giles remembered that he'd promised to introduce her to Stella.

"Stella - this is Thisbe Eversley; she's one of our fiddlers and one of your great admirers."

Stella said, "How nice. But why?"

Thisbe picked up a mug, and said, "Milk, sugar?"

"Just black," said Stella.

Then Thisbe rushed on, her words tumbling over each other.

"I've been working at your second quartet, I studied it, and we played it when I was at the Academy. I wish I could play it properly, but..."

"No time to live as well as to play in an orchestra?"

"Just about that." She felt that an oracle had spoken to her, and she went away smiling.

The huge, cavernous building was half dark. There were a few people dotted about in the stalls, and four or five of them, having seen Stella's arrival, emerged from the shadowy distance and were soon round her, all pupils, all admirers.

Giles said, "You'll see how hard we've been working," and went on to the stage, while the others crowded round Stella and her score.

Francis said quietly to Alice, "Shall we move back, then they can sit with her?"

"Of course. I'd rather be further away, anyway."

They carried their mugs with them, and watched both the group round Stella and the orchestra re-assembling with interest. They were not used to being at rehearsals, and both of them found the casual clothes and the grouping of the players as they gossiped before moving into their seats like a scene in a play.

That evening, after dinner, the Residents sat round the television set to do their duty by Stella, as Liz Grindel said. She did add, rather wistfully, "Well, I would have gone to the concert, if I could have done so without all the difficulties." There were some yawns, some books were opened, a faint unease among the viewers, as the cameras shifted from a flute player's fingers to a double bass, to the first violins, the beautiful, smooth movement of bows, then to the conductor. The music was turned low, but every now and then enough came through to produce foot tapping, and then some complaints.

"We ought to be listening, properly."

"Why? I wish we hadn't got to have this programme."

"Nobody has to have it, but we all want to see Dame Stella don't we?"

"Not so much want as must."

"Now I, well - Oh, I think we should."

The words criss-crossed the undertone of music for nearly half an hour. The Residents had not, of course, come in at the beginning of the concert, the first two short pieces had played quietly to an array of empty armchairs.

After the last note of the fifth *Brandenburg concerto*, Henry said pettishly, lighting a cigarette, "I don't like Bach really, why should one?"

He put down his *London Standard* with a sigh as Stella, Francis and John Delavell were discovered sitting together. Stella sat very upright, and marvellously still. "All that fuss about her back," said Henry.

But, lit by someone who obviously liked her, she looked splendid. The talk was not too technical, Francis asked her sensible questions, and John Delavell steered her away from indiscretions. It had taken half a morning to film, but the result lasted a bare ten minutes. When it ended there was a short talk by John Delavell about the new work to follow, Stella's "Night Sounds", to which the Residents paid little attention, beyond talking in half whispers. Then the Albert Hall came swimming back on to the screen, the Prommers talking, moving about, some lying on the floor, some fanning themselves, the orchestra coming back onto the stage, and while they took their places, a quick flick round the auditorium, a drift of faces turned to each other, unaware that they were in view of another, watching audience, then coming to rest for a moment on Stella, Francis and Alice, and several young men, unknown to the Residents. Then the lights dimmed, the conductor came on, bowed, turned to the orchestra, and the bows began to move over the strings, and the Residents began to gossip again as their attention wandered.

Francis was aware that tension, almost a visible cloud round Stella, had vanished. She was not only listening, she had become the music, she was so utterly concentrated. He, released from the nervousness that had held him, too, on her behalf, started to listen. The music, and he knew that the name of the piece was his guidance, became a strange mixture of sight and sound, creating a darkness in which solos of flute, clarinet, then a harp, then the sound of a viola, leading downwards to a 'cello, then to the basses, became almost visible, a widening of the ear's domain and, for him, letting in vision. A sky by Wright of Derby, an El Greco storm, and his own memories of woods at night.

For Alice the pattern was different, her senses were concentrated into hearing. The way the sounds crossed, answered, lifted or subsided were entirely comprehensible in their own idiom. It was not a long work, but one of great clarity, intense concentration of experience, beautiful in a cold way, alluring, dangerous. Those words came to her afterwards. During the performance all she had begun to realise at the morning rehearsal was communicated fully, for what had seemed unfamiliar then she now felt she had known always. It was, she guessed, a particularly good first performance. The total absorption of the audience, the stillness of the Prommers had created an answering intensity to that of the musicians.

The piece ended with a flute solo, following a short passage with harp and clarinet from which the flute disentangled and moved into a solitude where it seemed to meet silence rather than to end.

There was a pause of several seconds before Giles put down his baton, and the applause started. Stella was absolutely still, then as if the clapping had broken into her own silence, she turned to Francis. "They brought it off, they really did," she said.

Giles had bowed to the applause, and then he crossed the stage, behind the first fiddles. As they'd arranged in the morning, Francis helped Stella to her feet, and Giles led her on to the platform. Instead of a cloak she had an immense trail of emerald chiffon over her black dress, which streamed behind her as she walked. She bowed to the audience, kissed Giles, shook hands with the leader, bowed too, to the audience sitting behind the orchestra, and as Giles brought the players to their feet, she bowed again to the hall. As Giles led her off the stage, the orchestra, sitting once more, applauded her. The delicate sound of tapping bows could be heard above the clapping, and the air seemed electric with excitement to Francis.

Alice said, "She's happy."

"Was it as amazing as I think it was?"

"As good as could be. Very much her own voice, and the solo parts were so well played."

They were able to slip out, fairly unobtrusively, and while Giles returned to end the concert with a Haydn Symphony, they joined Stella in the artists' room. She was excited, but thankful to be sitting down again. She said, "And the odd thing, Alice, is that I'm fearfully hungry."

"There's some whisky, and I got some sandwiches organised."

"Thank goodness. I want to see them all after this, and I'd have been in a bad way if I was not nourished."

They drank their whiskies, and were able to relax and gossip about nothing in particular till the players came off the platform, and Giles brought in those who had played the solo parts in her work. Then all tension vanished in thanks. As the players left to find their cars, hurrying home for a few hours before they would be back at rehearsals next morning, and Giles went off to the conductor's room to change, some of Stella's students and a crowd of old friends came in, and she was besieged.

Alice was worried that all this excitement might be too much for her. Francis was reassuring. "It's nourishing her, look how she's sparkling."

Indeed she was, as if all her aches, all the troubles with her back had never been.

Neither Alice nor Francis knew many of the people there, though several of those who had also been at the rehearsal in the morning and recognised them, came over to talk. Two of her students, a man and a girl stayed, and both were saying how much they had learned from her. "Though," said the girl, a lively freckled little creature with an American accent, "she can give one hell, sometimes. Mark copies for her as well, so he probably knows this work better than any of us. It's amazing how much she can do with so little, and it's never thin." Her words fell over themselves as she waved her hands about in emphasis.

The narrow room was getting very hot and smokey by the time Giles came back, changed from tails into a blue linen jacket.

"What about supper, Stella?" he asked, as if he was quite unaware of her fragility.

"Lovely," she said, "oh yes."

"You'll come, of course." He invited Alice and Francis, "and Mark, what about you and Annie?"

"May we?" Annie, the enthusiastic girl, was excited at the prospect.

It was Mark who helped Stella to her feet, and unobtrusively picked up her stick, found her bag and supported her up the flight of stairs to the artists' entrance. Though it was half an hour since the concert had ended, there was a small crowd still waiting outside. When Stella and then Giles appeared they started clapping and asking for autographs, but Mark steered her through the press, and Giles said firmly, "Not tonight," to the autograph hunters. Alice and Francis followed, and Giles spoke to the driver of the car, and then collected the two young ones.

"I booked a table on spec." he said. "It's at Fabrizio's, not far from Marion's, I thought. See you there."

The party was lively enough. Stella was still excited, nourished, as Francis had realised, by excitement and pleasure. But after an hour or so she turned to Alice.

"I feel like Cinderella, must go back before the magic ends."

She looked suddenly very white and lined, the beauty that belonged to the music was yielding to exhaustion, and her back had begun to hurt again.

"It was wonderful, Giles," she murmured, as she got into the car, which Francis had organised to wait for them. Then to Alice, "I wish Lalla had been there, I wish she wasn't away."

But it was all right when she got back, for Mrs. Miles was waiting, and able to tell her how much she'd enjoyed the television, as she helped her to bed, and finally put out the light.

Stella found sleep evaded her, and she longed for some other human to be there. Sleeping alone after all the excitement was unbearable. That, more than aching back and arm, hurt and defeated her.

"I wouldn't have cared a damn who it was," she told Alice in the morning. "I needed a man last night, I needed anyone, absolutely anyone."

Alice, who had not experienced deprivation and who had not, either, experienced the heightened tension of creation and performance, was dismayed at the thought that, battered and worn by age and pain as Stella appeared, it was unsatisfied flesh rather than fulfilled achievement that seemed to be uppermost in her mind. She tried to think of how to answer suitably, and realised that she was rather shocked, and then dismayed by this reaction. For why on earth should Stella remain so creative, and yet be beyond physical passions to match those of her mind?

"Alice," Stella said, apprehending her thoughts, "I still have those 'stirrings of noonday', and I bet you don't think that, among all your lot here, are cravings and fallings in and out of love, and anguishes and jealousies that have nothing to do with memories, and faithful widowhood and all that acceptable, sentimental stuff, suitable to the penning up of the lot of them in this geriatric nursery."

"Well," Alice saw justice in the accusation. "I suppose I haven't thought of age like that. Really I've been looking for cushions for the disabilities more than anything."

"Very praiseworthy, very necessary. Don't think that I'm ungrateful. It's been marvellous for me, for a bit, and I know that no one on earth would consider making love to me, now. I would even despise them if they did, but it doesn't mean that it isn't what I'd have liked most in the world last night." She paused, then said,

"People like you and Francis can't imagine, I think, don't begin to know what real loneliness is, and I'm not talking about space for work in one's life. Married people, particularly happily married ones, if there are any, are another tribe you know. Like all alien tribes one admires, hates, envies, loves some of the ones one meets, in one sense fears them for their inward looking, in another sense despises their safety, in a sense is unreasonably jealous - "

"Always?"

"No, of course not. I love you and I love Francis for his poems. It's old age too, everything is inaccessible now, all that's lost to me, and not to you."

They stared at each other across the gulf that Stella had, as it were, pointed out lying terrifyingly between them. Stella went on, going back to Alice's question.

"Of course not always, of course not when you are so good to me. I'm tired and tetchy and aware of mortality today."

"Have you seen the papers?" Alice offered a way out of their predicament. "Francis was going to bring them all round. He's doing another BBC job today, and planned to come here with them this evening. About six, I think."

Stella was grateful for this means of retreat.

"Good. I'll be up to the critics by then. They'll probably have missed all the point of it, though."

"Not 'The Times'. I brought that for you. I expect you'll want to go quietly today, so I'll leave it for you."

"Bless you Alice, you're being saintly, of course."

But, as she left, Alice wondered if, in this context, that was a synonym for boring.

To everyone's surprise Stella seemed suddenly much better after the concert. In the next week she decided to go back to her flat as soon as possible, and she found that she could write a little more each day. She was restive, but much politer to everyone in the house than she had been before, as if they had become bearable to her now that she would soon be leaving them, and never have to see or to think of any of them again.

By one of the lucky chances that usually came her way, in the nick of time, she found, through one of her pupils, a young man who was out of work, loved cooking, liked old ladies, but not music, so would not be a bother wanting to discuss or to comment. He was delighted by the prospect of looking after Stella, shopping and cooking for her. Cleaning he didn't much like, but doubtless that side of the job would, as he said, work out. So Alice, relieved of the business of organising home helps and everything else, merely had to drive her home from Marion's. "Some time next week, I think," Stella said. "I'll fix it with Terence." He was the young man. "My Find," as Stella called him.

Alice did not tell Francis about her conversation with Stella the morning after the concert. She felt that it would be like stripping her naked. That bold design, brilliant cloaks and trails of chiffon put aside to show crêpey flesh and knots and webs of darkened veins. She had had an echo in her mind which she could not trace at first, and then realised it was Villon, "La Belle Hëaumiere", of whom she was thinking, the harsh and tender description of the girl who had been beautiful and now was old, wrinkled, with gnarled hands. She re-read the poem, and it made her cry. She doubted if Stella knew it, but it made her think of all she had said that morning about the old being another tribe. She wondered, then, about Lalla and Tom, if they had come across Villon yet, and she thought that this poem was something that she should show them.

She realised that she had been so preoccupied by the concert, the notices, the business of Stella's plans that she'd entirely neglected Maria. She telephoned one morning when Francis was working.

"Maria - how are you?"

Maria had been glad not to have seen Alice, and was grateful for the interval of no communication, but now, again, she found that she wanted to talk to her, said that she was fine, but that she hadn't yet answered Charles's letter.

"It's extraordinary, the longer I put off writing the less I want to write to him. I can't think of anything to say."

"What about his things? I suppose he'll want his clothes and hasn't he got books and - oh, I suppose things like binoculars?"

Maria started laughing.

"Alice you're so tidy. Yes, of course he has. He only took the one suitcase of stuff. You know, for a week. So everything's here. I keep looking at it all, and it makes me furious, but it's funny too, in a bleak way. I keep wondering how he's managing without this and that. And then I get furious about being left with it all. People who leave their wives like this ought to take every scrap of everything with them. It feels provisional like this, and I don't like it."

"What are you going to do about it?"

"I don't know, I absolutely don't know. I keep going to cinemas because I can't think what to do about anything."

She sounded rather desperate.

"Come to lunch," Alice reacted immediately.

"Oh yes. I would like to see a human face again, particularly yours."

Maria spoke without thinking of Francis, and then realised that she'd probably have to see him too. They hadn't met since she had lunched with him, since all that followed. She had no idea how she would feel when they met again, nor how he would feel, nor was she sure how perceptive Alice was, and if it was another, unwished-for drama ahead. But she was lonely; everyone else at this moment seemed like acquaintances on the fringe of a life she had already left, almost like people who had seen her off at some airport after a short visit to their country.

Alice was in the kitchen, reading, while she kept guard over the fish for lunch, as both cats had decided that it was too damp to stay out. She had put everything more or less out of their reach, but both were capable of getting on to the top of the fridge, or anywhere else, no shelf was safe. Lewis had been known to open the warming drawer below the oven to remove six chops, hidden there to cool. Luckily he had left the drawer open, and a few small bones on the floor, giving Alice warning to make other and hasty arrangements for her party. At this moment he was safely asleep, but Amy sat on the kitchen table being affectionate. If Alice removed her hand from stroking her to turn over a page she leant forward and patted her, paw delicately curved, and claws sheathed. It was a charming gesture but became extremely boring when too often repeated, putting Alice in the wrong, making her feel unappreciative and even neglectful of such a well disposed cat as Amy knew herself to be. So, she was glad when Maria arrived for even Amy knew that front door bells have to be answered.

"Once this meeting is over," Maria said to herself as she stood on the doorstep, "it'll be all right. I shan't think about it any more, I shan't feel embarrassed, and after all. . . " But at that moment Alice opened the door.

"Come in out of the rain."

With the heavy grey sky every colour in the garden seemed rich and brilliant, having the same quality of brightness that pebbles and seaweeds have under water, and lose so quickly when beached and dry.

Maria's scarlet umbrella was too bright for Alice's front garden of blues and purples, pinks and crimsons, in the pots on the steps, like an intrusion of scarlet geraniums. It was soon out of sight, dripping onto tiles by the back garden door, and Maria, dressed in cream, sat by the table with a glass in her hand. Amy left, slightly offended, and sat primly on the floor.

"There was another letter from Charles, second post." Maria plunged in to talk with a fine cover-up subject.

"Asking why you hadn't written to him, I suppose?"

"Yes, worse, he's coming back, to talk, to collect his things, to arrange; to divorce, I suppose."

Alice thought to herself that Francis would deal with this situation better than she could.

"When?" was all she could think of saying.

"Next week, next Monday. He'll come in, you know, and want a bath and breakfast, which will be as it always was, and then he'll spend ages on the telephone, and I'll be hanging about, and we'll go out to lunch, and he'll be jet lagged, and spend the afternoon sleeping. And what the hell do I do about all that?"

"Surely he'll go to an hotel?"

"I doubt it - if he wants to talk."

Francis heard their voices and came in from his study. He, too, had been wondering how he and Maria would manage this meeting, and he too was relieved when Alice greeted him with the news of Charles's letter as he crossed the room to give Maria the usual, friendly hug. The trouble was that each of them longed to kiss properly, rather than to exchange a perfunctory peck, rather less of a kiss than had been usual. Alice did not notice as her mind was busy with Charles's return.

"Do you think that he wants to come back for good?"

"No. I'm sure not. Here's his letter."

She gave it to Francis rather than to Alice, as if he, rather than she, was her natural adviser, and then wondered if that instinctive gesture had been a mistake.

Francis read it and passed it to Alice.

"Dearest Maria," she read. "Why haven't you written to me? I have to go to England, Flight - " Oh, I can't be bothered with that, thought Alice. "Arriving Heathrow on the 28th, 9.00 a.m. Will come home at once." Home? thought Alice, crossly. "Much to discuss, arrangements, and all that. Love, Charles"

"Well. I don't see what's to be done. You'll just have to see how it goes."

"I wish he wasn't coming, though. I do not know how one meets in this sort of circumstance."

"I don't suppose that he knows that, either," said Francis.

Both he and Maria felt their complicity in discussing how first meetings in new circumstances were to be achieved. After half an hour spent talking about it no conclusion was reached.

"After all," Alice ended her share of the conversation, "we're talking about moods to come, and discussing principles of good or bad or indifferent behaviour isn't relevant."

"And, in any case, good, bad and indifferent are in the eye of the beholder, aren't they?"

"You're no help at all," Maria was by now very much more cheerful.

"I have no principles, except to refuse to wash his shirts when he arrives with - oh, but," her face fell as she remembered. "There'll probably be only one, for bloody Désirée will have sent him off with a suitcase full of clean ones."

"One problem less," said Alice.

Chapter 6

For Tom and Lalla the fortnight passed all too quickly. Golden days, Etruscan tombs and the little winged and golden horses of Tarquinia. The late afternoon view of Orvieto on its hill top, like a medallion in its perfection of golden light, tall plants of fennel by the wayside with tiny brown snails decorating the dry stems. Assisi, noble and so much older than they'd expected, wine and figs, and sometimes bullock carts piled with grapes, the bullocks' horns wreathed with vine leaves.

"I never thought we'd see that sort of thing; I'd supposed it would be nothing but lorries."

"The bullock carts are narrow enough to drive between the vines - much more practical," said Lalla.

They were happy and loving and ready to be enchanted and surprised by everything they saw, as if a haze of magic hung over every day as it did over each night. They talked about the old people they saw in the country places, who were, as far as they could judge, still involved with whatever work was going on or, if infirm, sitting in the shade under trellises, watching with stern and critical interest.

"Though it's impossible to tell, isn't it, how old they are. It's a different sort of wear and tear in the country," Tom said.

"Probably younger than they look. It must be a very hard life."

"It's like looking at another century, all the black clothes and toothlessness."

"I expect they think that we're the odd ones, all our lot. I wonder if they wish they had as easy a life as we do, or if they have the usual thoughts about the young going to the dogs. That's what the elders and betters used to think, isn't it?"

"General trend," Tom agreed. "In fact, as far as I can see they ought to understand us better than we can be expected to understand them. After all they've risen from the ranks as it were, or the factory floor, or the apprenticeships, and we are not very far from the bottom, so they've all experienced our time of life and we, thank heaven, haven't yet got to theirs."

"Jealous?" Lalla asked. They were sitting in a cafe in Perugia, finishing an agreeable meal, a large, but rapidly diminishing bowl of figs on the table, with glasses of water and cups of espresso coffee. "Youth wasted on the young?" she went on. "I've certainly thought that that must be a point of view held by people who discovered pleasure rather late in life."

"How do you feel about going back to England? I'm almost looking forward to it. This has been too good to be true."

"Pessimist." Lalla helped herself to another fig.

"Oh yes, of course. Not quite such a pessimist as Francis is. I do not think that he sees any hope for anything anywhere, just the stoic virtues to sustain him in an age of wanton destruction."

"Really, as bad as that? Do you suppose that's why Alice concerns herself so much?"

"Don't know. She does seem concerned. It could all be part of the same thing, less stoic, feather beds and bunches of roses for the discomforted. Immediate help and succour."

"Oh, I should think so. She's no fool, or Francis wouldn't have been married to her for so long."

"You do admire him, don't you?"

"Yes. I think he believes the Taliesin story, the one Graves told in *The White Goddess*, about the wrong child, the servant stirring the witch's cauldron, and accidentally tasting the brew and getting the gift meant for the witch's son, of understanding the other languages, all that creatures say. Then the witch hunting him through all the transformations, bird, and her pursuit as a hawk, hare, and she a hound, fish and she a diving bird, and finally a grain of wheat that fell into the river and was swallowed by a salmon, and then the salmon cooked for supper at the castle, and the grain being eaten by the Queen who immediately conceived a child, and he, having been all through the transformations, could become the great poet."

Lalla had not read *The White Goddess*, and had no inclination to do so. "But, in all those transformations he was the hunted one. So where does that leave the poet? It doesn't sound either princely or bardic to me," she said.

"True. I hadn't thought of it like that. The important part of the story seems to me that the poet has to be able to become everything, to feel like a fly or a lion or a grain of wheat."

"Method acting." Lalla dismissed Tom's argument, and asked for more coffee.

As they were going to fly from Pisa they had decided to spend the last night of their holiday there and to enjoy the benefit of the full moon to look at the Duomo, Baptistry and Leaning Tower in that magic light for a final treat.

"John Evelyn said, when he was here, in goodness, when was it? 1644 or so, that the Campo Santo is all earth, galley loads, he said, brought from Jerusalem which consume dead bodies in the space of forty hours. Carcofagus was his word."

"More homework than I expected." She was rather bored by all this information, but she said laughing, "Why do we bother with crematoria if Jerusalem earth is so tidy? Do you suppose that it's still usable? If so, wouldn't it be more sensible and much cheaper?"

371

"Probably it doesn't work any more. Gone, like will o' the wisps, and St. Elmo's Fire or unicorns and mermaids. Anyway, he talked about the Echo, and that will still be there for us."

"Echoes, echoes, I think that's what we're exploring, people listening to their own echoes," said Lalla.

"Take time while time is, or time will away," was Tom's contribution as he paid the bill.

They came back to London cheerful, and full of travellers' tales, and with large bottles of Duty Free Campari, for two days more of freedom in London, unpacking, settling into the small flat acquired by Tom, arranging their notes, and generally changing their pace.

Lalla telephoned to Alice almost as soon as they arrived. "We're home."

"Welcome, welcome." Alice was delighted to hear Lalla's voice. "Will you have time to come to see us soon?"

"Of course, and to bring back your books. We were very glad to have them."

"Why don't you come to supper on Monday. Then you needn't bother about shopping or anything."

"Lovely. Half a minute. Tom the Dulacs want us to go to supper on Monday."

"Yes, yes." He sounded pleased.

"We'd love to. About eight?"

"Yes, and all news when we meet."

Alice had forgotten that Monday was the day on which Charles was to arrive. When she remembered she did not know whether to expect

Maria to appear on her doorstep in a rage, to have a report of a reconciliation, or to hear nothing for several days. She was certainly anxious about Maria, about her future, which, she supposed might well be decided in the first moments of Charles's return. "I can't imagine how I'd feel if I was waiting for you after you had gone off with Joanna-Désirée," she said at breakfast.

"I doubt if I should have gone to Australia in the first place," Francis said mildly.

"What does one say when a man comes home, after all that?"

"I suppose she'll know at once if he looks on it as an escapade or if it is serious."

"She'll tell you," Alice said.

"Oh, she'll tell us both I expect, or whichever of us is in and available." Francis hoped that it would be Alice she found at home.

But Charles did not arrive on the day he had planned. Air traffic control strikes delayed his plane. He telephoned to say that he was in Frankfurt, would get back as soon as possible, he didn't know exactly. Then the call was cut off. Maria was furious, and furious with herself for minding so much that the moment of meeting, which she had nerved herself to face, was going to be at some unpredictable time. She went to a cinema, had a meal in a Chinese restaurant, then went to another film, and so home through the blue half-darkness of the summer evening. Neither film had captured enough of her attention to divert her thoughts, nor did she sleep well.

Lalla's first question had been about Stella. Alice and Francis told her about the concert, and about Terence.

"They moved on Thursday," Alice said, "at least Stella did. Terence moved in earlier in the week. I went to see him at the flat to take flowers and things. It all looked splendid, very clean and polished, and inviting. It was wonderful to see her pleasure when she arrived."

"Marion's will be extraordinary without her," Lalla said, "but I do long to see Minette again."

"I fear she's put on weight while you've been away."

"No walks? And those awful ginger chocolates."

Tom said, "We've been away for only two weeks, and the time flew by, though each day seemed enormous because we did so many things, though our sightseeing seemed slow-motion, in a way."

"So were our meals," reminded Lalla.

"Holidays are strange," Francis agreed. "It's the distance or the change of sound; and a different language, seem to make a different reality."

"And having nothing one needs to do, all choice."

"Alice likes having her breakfast on a sunny balcony, eating peaches and reading Henry James while I go to the bank for her," Francis explained.

"We've done a little work, though," Tom said. "We decided that we couldn't go on for ever collecting scraps of information and observation. So much work has already been done on the age concern front, so we've decided to write all we can about Fred, about his sort of life before and after his accident, and about his Home and his companions, and, if we may, about Dame Stella and about Marion's."

Alice looked at Francis, troubled about confidentiality, he diagnosed.

"All disguised as Xs and Ys," Tom said quickly. "With all we've learned about the rest as a sort of background."

"You see one character with very little, and one with a very great deal," Lalla added.

"Any conclusions?" Francis asked, thinking of his own work.

"Yes," both said at once.

"Well?" Francis leant forward as if he wanted to catch every breath of meaning.

"That age is a clarification of character and a physical disguise." Tom answered for himself and for Lalla.

"We agreed on that," Lalla said. "It's as far as we can see as observers."

"You have had a lot of confidences," Alice said. "So the evidence is direct."

"I suppose that is as near as one can get," Tom answered. "Until we are old ourselves."

"So the best that we can do is to alleviate the discomforts of the disguise?" Alice asked, as if concluding the evidence.

"Aspects of reality aren't the whole thing." Francis had been thinking, as they spoke, that these conclusions were simple and sensible, devoted diagnoses of conditions. His own conclusions were different and in no way practical. He was trying to understand not what could be done for the Freds, the Hatchetts, the Marys, Lizs and Henrys, even for the Stellas, but to see how it felt to be people after chances and hopes, after even looking forward, had ceased. When all that had been future had slipped, almost unnoticed, into becoming past. How to see that past as a part of a whole daytime of seasons and emotions, and how to relinquish it for an unknown something, or for annihilation, while the flesh mourned lost powers and pleasures.

"Actually it's almost complete now. We've both been writing a good deal, and we have to collate our notes." Lalla looked at Tom for approval.

"Mayhew has been a good teacher," Tom said. "We've tried to be as exact and as careful."

"May we see it when you've finished?" Alice was still anxious about Stella appearing as an example to be made public.

"We were going to ask if you would," Tom answered.

Lalla looked at her watch.

"I've got to be at Marion's by nine sharp," she said, "so perhaps we'd better go now, and it is kind of you to have us, and to let us talk so much."

"You'll go to see Stella soon, won't you? She missed you very much, but I think that she's doing quite well with Terence."

"She'll bully him and he'll adore it," Francis reassured Lalla. "So don't worry about her, but go and tell her about Italy."

Francis had gone to the BBC next morning, and Alice was at the hairdressers when Maria came to see them. She had gone for a walk, tired of waiting for Charles, tired of killing time, wondering what to do or to say. She went to Regent's Park and walked about for what seemed a very long time. Then she decided that she could not bear being alone any longer. She had supposed that either Francis or Alice would be in. Finding that there was no one at their house, only the cats, sleeping agreeably on the doorstep, and not disposed to be sociable, she went home.

Charles had arrived and she found him having a bath. His clothes were strewn about the room and there was a steamy smell of rose-geranium coming from the open bathroom door.

"Here I am," he said, and realising it was a statement of the obvious, he added, "Bloody awful journey. Where have you been?"

"Does that concern you?" She surprised herself by saying the words, and by the chilly sound of her voice.

"Well, yes, it does." He got out of the bath, wrapped himself in a towel, and kissed her warmly.

"Charles."

"Yes?"

"Well, well. Where are we? What are we going to do? What are you going to do?"

She sat down on the foot of the bed and started to cry. He sat down beside her and put his arm round her. She cried against his wet shoulder.

"I haven't got a hanky," he said. "Shall I get you a tissue?"

"Don't be so silly. I mean, I don't mean I want to cry. It's just seeing you here when I'd got used to the idea of never seeing you again, and then I find you in the bath."

"Whatever has that got to do with anything? Of course I wanted a bath after all that ridiculous journey. You don't mind my having a bath, do you?" He sounded aggrieved and Maria started to laugh. Suddenly they were both in a stage of hopeless giggles. Maria went on crying at the same time. Charles disentangled himself and went to the kitchen and came back with glasses of white wine, faintly misty from the fridge. "Good. You still keep glasses in the fridge, I see." "Why ever not? Why should I change my habits in a month?" "Good God, is it only a month?" "Just about that." They sat and stared at each other, abashed by all that had changed since they had last seen each other.

Suddenly Charles said, "God, it's good to see you again, Maria."

She looked at him in surprise.

"But - Joanna?"

"Yes, Joanna. That's quite different. And what can I say about that?

But it doesn't make any difference to being glad to see you."

"Oh, Charles, we're hopeless. I'm glad to see you again too."

"It would be rather extraordinary if we weren't. After all this time."

"What time? Since you've been away?"

"No, all the time we've put up with each other."

"Is that what we were doing?" Maria spoke seriously.

"For quite a lot of years I'd say. Remember all the places that bored you?"

"And all the people I liked and you found dull."

"Just so. I think it takes this to make us both find out that we are glad to see each other."

"Ridiculous," Maria said. "Bloody ridiculous. I find that I like you, and I don't love you." She looked at him, rather sadly.

"How chilly that sounds, Charles, but I think that it's what I've been feeling for ages."

"Less awful than loving and not liking."

"Yes." She hoped that this was not how he felt about Joanna.

"It's all rather improbable, but I am glad to see you." He emphasised 'am'. The present tense prevailed for the rest of an oddly amiable, rather cousinly day.

As evening approached both Maria and Charles began to feel that the other should say something about what should happen next.

At last Charles said, "I'll get a room somewhere."

Maria said, "Wouldn't the spare room do?" He brightened at once.

"May I?"

"Why not?"

"Splendid. Where shall we dine?"

There was a complicity in their treatment of each other on this exchange, as if there were, at least in their minds, an audience for their words. Perhaps distant Joanna; perhaps, for Maria, Francis.

Over dinner Charles said, "Joanna wants me to go to see her mother."

"Do you think that's a good idea? You know what she used to say about her?"

"Oh yes I know. It must have been an awful childhood. All that music being in the foreground all the time."

"I suppose the only child anyone ever understands completely is their own childhood." Maria did not much like children, she had always supposed that this was because she had had no pleasure in being a child, believing that a grown-up life was a far better thing, and the sooner it began the better. Charles let this go.

"Well, she wants me to see her, a sort of peace-making embassy. So I suppose I had better. I've got the address. I expect you know the latest news on that front, don't you, from Alice?"

"Oh yes. And she's probably approachable because I know she's very glad to be back at her flat again."

"So, I'd better go, I suppose. I wish you'd come too, but," as he caught her look of amazed amusement he stopped and added lamely, "of course that's impossible. But what have I let myself in for?"

"Trouble", said Maria.

When Charles reached the house overlooking Primrose Hill he was feeling distinctly nervous. It was a tall house, built for solid, mid-Victorian comfort, with big windows, diminishing in size with each floor; bars suggested that long ago the top floor had been a nursery. He stood and stared at it for a few minutes, wondering on which floor he would find the alarming mother Joanna had described in various ways. 'Unfeeling' had been the word that predominated, 'selfish' had also been a fairly regular adjective, and recently 'old' used in a more kindly way. He had brought some flowers, fairly expensive roses so carefully wrapped in cellophane that they had no apparent individual life, but were a yellow blob, emerging from green in their glistening cornucopia. There were five bells. Fortescue, in red ink, was the second from the bottom.

His ring was answered by a buzz. He pushed the door, which was heavy, and went in to a long passage-like hall, painted a heavy cream colour, carpet tiles of a reddish brown covered the floor. As he entered, a door halfway down the hall opened and a thin young man with yellow hair said, "You looking for Dame Stella? Come in." He went into a tiny square in which three doors were closed; the fourth, a kitchen, contrived, Charles guessed, from what must have been a large cupboard, was open and disclosed a neat arrangement of wall cupboards, and the equipment for anyone who clearly had no interest in more than basic necessities of survival. A toaster and an electric kettle were the obvious props.

"Is Dame Stella at home?"

Charles heard his voice becoming idiotically formal.

"Sure. Who shall I say?"

"Oh, oh, say it's Charles."

Terence opened the door on the right, and closed it behind him. Charles heard a murmur, and the door reopened, held formally wide to let him in.

The room was large. He saw the grand piano by the window, and a mass of pictures, bookshelves, piles of books on the floor, plants on the window sill, and then Stella, sitting on a small sofa. She was wearing a sort of dressing gown of dark orange, and on the table beside her was a telephone, a heap of books, a bottle of whisky, a half filled glass, and all the odds and ends that suggested a plan for having everything she might possibly need within reach.

She looked him up and down rather as if she was measuring him - for heroic possibilities? For a wedding suit? For words to open a conversation?

"So you're Charles," she said.

He stood, feeling inadequate as he had not felt since his schooldays.

"Yes. I hope that you don't mind my calling on you. I wanted to see you, and I thought that you might refuse to see me if I telephoned."

"It's not too late to refuse to talk with you now."

She spoke severely. Then she saw the roses.

"Well, sit down as you are here," she said.

"I hope you like yellow roses?" He put the bunch on the table.

"They're the only shop roses I do like; they have some scent. They've managed to breed every vestige of smell out of most of the commercial bouquet supplies." She called Terence.

"Be a love and put them in water for me."

Terence collected the bunch and asked, as if reminding her of hospitality, "Shall I bring another glass and some ice?"

"Oh. Charles, would you like a drink?"

Grasping for salvation he heard his voice saying "Yes" very firmly.

"You can pour out for yourself." Terence had obviously had the green bowl of ice and the glass ready to bring in. "Do you want water with it, or something?"

"Oh, the rocks will be fine."

"Well, so here you are, and what do you want to say to me?"

"Joanna wanted me to bring her love to you, and I, naturally, well, naturally, was anxious to meet you."

"Really? Mothers-in-law aren't particularly interesting I should have thought, in your circumstances, that is, if you are going to marry her. Are you?"

"I - I - we - we hope so." Charles had managed to drink about half of the whisky in his glass and felt its comforting familiarity adding a little courage to his consciousness of being unfavourably placed, facing the light to which Stella had her back.

"But I suppose there are difficulties? Alice's friend, your wife, how does she see the situation?"

Charles had no intention of telling Stella that Maria liked him, but had ceased, so she said, to love him.

"We have not discussed the future," he said. "Of course she and Joanna have met, when she was in Australia with me." The 'shes' seemed to have become confused. He drank some more whisky.

Stella said, "Joanna seems to be happy with you. If she's telling the truth, and she is happy with you, it will be a great change for the better. She's been a most difficult woman. But I dare say she's made a more suitable arrangement this time." Charles hoped that this meant that Stella was approving him.

"I hope that she will be happy" he said. He was, by now, looking at Stella to see if there was any likeness to her that Joanna had inherited. He had not, at first, been aware of Stella's crippled hands, and they shocked him. He saw too, that her face was heavily lined round her eyes, that the corners of her mouth were turned down, whether with pain or disapproval he did not know. She returned his look. "Very ordinary," she was thinking. "It won't hurt Alice's friend to lose one like that." It was a sharp summing up, for Charles at his best was an attractive, kind and direct man. There were times when ambition became toughness, and there was a rapacious look about him, a streak of successful gambler, a buccaneering streak, but none of that was apparent to Stella. She did, however, recognise that he was someone for whom her work, her values would be of no importance, interest, or reality. He was the kind of man for whom she had no use at all.

Meanwhile, both were striving for a good-mannered way of spending the shortest time possible in each other's company.

"When are you going back to Australia?"

"As soon as I have arranged my affairs here. I hope that will not take long."

"So you plan to settle in Australia?"

"I think that is a good idea. My wife - Maria, I mean - never liked the life there. She's much happier in London."

"Geography is a problem," Stella conceded. "And Joanna is much happier in Australia. What luck for you."

This brought the conversation to another halt. Fortunately Terence broke the silence which had lasted for nearly thirty seconds, seeming to Charles more like thirty minutes, by coming in with the roses which he had arranged charmingly, having clipped off the excessive leaves, in one of Stella's treasured Persian pots.

"Very nice Terence, very nice indeed." Terence, realising the taut atmosphere, filled up their glasses before he went back to the kitchen where, judging by delicious smells, he was doing some creative cooking in spite of the limited paraphernalia.

"What I came to tell you," Charles said, "is that I will look after Joanna well. I promise you."

"Oh yes, Joanna. She seems to be adept at being looked after. I don't, of course, know her very well. She has been away for so long. She has, I have always thought, rather limited aspirations."

She waited with malicious pleasure to see how he would answer this. But he was saved from having to deny or to be modest, for was he, he thought furiously, a limited expectation, by Alice's arrival? Both he and Stella had heard the bell, the subsequent buzz, and a murmur of voices outside.

"Hello," said Alice, "how are you Terence?"

"Fine. I'm glad to see you, there's a freeze-up going on in there."

"Oh dear, who's freezing?"

"Well, it's a man called Charles, came without a date, and it doesn't seem a success. I've done my best with the whisky, but you're a much better bet."

"Oh God," said Alice. "She is expecting me, isn't she?"

"Oh yes. You're a lifeboat, I can tell you."

He grinned at her. "Go on - break it up."

"Hell. Oh, all right. Tell them I'm here."

She wanted a second's delay to think, and then she wanted to get this meeting with Charles over. When she went in, she could see that

384

Charles was getting up to go, and that he was as uncomfortable as she was feeling.

"Well, Charles," she said, and then crossed to kiss Stella.

"I was just going."

"Must you?" Stella was making it difficult, with pleasure, now she was sure that he would leave.

"Well, Alice, yes, Dame Stella," he had not finished his drink.

"You look well, Alice. How is Francis?"

"Well too, thank you, busy."

"Aren't we all? I have to get down to my bank, so please forgive me for rushing off just as you arrive."

She began to feel sorry for him.

"Of course. I didn't know that you had arrived. Didn't you have airport trouble?"

Steered on to a safe subject, he said that it had all been very tiresome, delays - the leave-taking was quickly over, and Terence let him out of the flat.

"Have you been grilling him Stella?"

"Not much. He's no loss to your friend, a rather corrupt character, too full of himself; came to say he'd look after that idiot daughter I have. Why shouldn't he? Silly bastard, I think, but like most of his kind he's half bully, half strawberry-milkshake. Not worth your friend's while I expect."

Alice laughed.

"I never thought of that mixture as a classification."

"I think that she'll be better off without him. People don't change; he's probably always been too easy, and she was at such close quarters that she never noticed before."

"It's hard to stand back and look if you're used to someone being so close." Alice agreed. "Poor Maria," she said, "it must be horrible to have such a changed view." Then, leaving this unprofitable subject, she asked, "How are you and Terence managing?"

"Pretty well. He's cleared out the little room and put all the music away in the top cupboards in my bedroom. Why anyone ever puts cupboards on top of built-in wardrobes that no one can reach without a ladder, God knows. But it's not bad now. He likes it, he says, and he's much more amusing than anyone was at the Home."

Stella looked sideways to see if Alice flinched at this description. She didn't, she was thinking of Maria and barely noticed.

"Good. Well don't bully him, Stella."

"I don't expect that I'll want to," Stella smiled, and Alice was touched by the sudden gentleness of her expression. Terence's kindness had wakened Stella's. The ill-assorted pair seemed to have settled down together, all the better, Alice thought, for Stella having found him for herself. They gossiped for an hour, but no more was said, to Alice's relief, about Charles or Maria or Joanna.

Once again Alice went home to find Maria in the garden. She thought it probable that Maria would be there, as soon as she knew that Charles had arrived. She wondered where he was staying, how Maria was feeling, and more immediately, how she and Francis would be involved.

"So what am I to do?" Maria had obviously reached the end of her story as Alice came out to join them.

"Begin again." Alice kissed Maria and sat down in a garden chair. Maria and Francis were sharing the garden seat.

"I found him having a bath," Maria began again. "It did seem reasonable, after the journey." Telling the story again to Alice, it seemed far less reasonable than it had at the time it happened. She felt that she should explain her feelings. Then she felt that she should not. And, at the same time, she realised that she had been enormously glad of his company having found the time that he had been away very empty.

All this was momentary. The cats, with unlikely tact, had filled the space between Alice's arrival and her own rather bald and jerky statements by insinuating themselves into the group round the garden table, showing off: Lewis by jumping on to the table and upsetting a glass with a bunch of dark pansies in it and Amy by climbing on to Maria's lap and demanding to be admired.

"Hell," Francis said. "You careless animal." But he knew that it was malicious intent not carelessness that had been at work.

"The point is," said Maria, stroking Amy, "I was rather glad to see him. It felt natural to have him about the place again."

Alice was still brooding about Stella's description of a bully with a milkshake heart, which she was longing to tell Francis. She mopped up the water with her handkerchief.

"Is he still staying?" she asked.

"Yes."

"For long?"

"He hasn't said."

"Haven't you asked him?"

"No. I don't think I want to know. I don't want him to talk about his plans, because they'll be about Joanna, so it's been a closed subject. After all, he arrived only yesterday."

"Are you getting fond of him again?"

Alice spoke lightly, but she wondered if the two of them were vacillating towards a reunion. It all seemed amazingly unclear and unsatisfactory. She felt that Stella's view of Charles had come into much sharper focus than her own acceptance of him as Maria's husband for years and years, for whom she had had kindly feelings rather than having any particular opinion. She had taken Maria's side, when he had written to say he was leaving her, if feeling outraged was taking sides. Now she was completely confused, wondering what was to Maria's advantage. So much that should, she felt, have long consideration was being hurried to conclusions. Did Maria want Charles to stay? Would it be a good thing if he did? Anyway, did it matter what her opinion was, even if it was asked for?

Francis was being as detached as he could manage to be. Maria, he saw, could be a danger if she was left alone, and the idea was both exciting and alarming. He didn't want to confuse his life with Alice by an involvement, for it could end only in pain and dissatisfaction, but it was going to be very difficult to avoid. He wished that Alice hadn't been out when Maria had come round, or that he had been.

Alice broke the silence with the news that Charles had been at Stella's flat when she went to see her, and found herself giving a lively account of Terence's cry for help, of Stella's frosty and dismissive behaviour, though not too much of that, and then of her account of her life in the flat with Terence.

"He's taught her to play backgammon," she said. "I think that it's the best thing that could have happened. He loves her pupils, and the social life, coffee and cake all day it seems, and some pretty advanced cooking. It's an amazing success. They're entertaining each other, providing an audience for each other. So, so far it's working beautifully."

She felt that she had been talking too much. Maria said, suddenly.

"Look, Alice. I think I've got to go away, let Charles finish whatever he's going to do, and arrange, and all that. Would you come somewhere for a week? Could you?"

"What, at once?" Alice was startled.

"Not this minute. Tomorrow?"

"Where?" Alice asked.

"Oh anywhere you like, west country perhaps, or Scotland, or the Isle of Wight?"

"Why not, Alice?" Francis felt that he should be helpful.

Alice had recognised that this was a cry for help from Maria. Inconvenient, of course. Francis didn't want to push her into a week of discussion about Maria's future, nor to make it difficult for her to agree to go. These sudden demands should be accepted or rejected on impulse. Like first impressions, the impulses were usually right. If Alice started to say things about having to see, and this and that would be difficult to get out of, he'd back her up, and say he'd forgotten about them. Otherwise, the weather was still balmy and golden and Alice liked the country in small doses, and there were always (she had an unfailing instinct for them) junk shops to be discovered.

"But have you and Charles settled anything?"

Alice thought of divorce and settlements and solicitors.

"I suppose our lawyers do all that."

"In that case. . ." Alice had caught Francis's eye, and knew that he'd accept whatever she felt she should do.

"Yes, Maria. I'll drive, you choose where we'll go."

She made her voice say the words as if she wanted to go.

Chapter 7

Lalla was welcomed back to Marion's as if she had been away for months. Her return was something fresh in a boring week, and it was not long before she was assimilated into the repetitive pattern of the days. She listened, she walked Minette, shopped, helped people to dress and to undress, spent time here, sewed on buttons there, changed library books, and began to wonder how much longer she could stand the people and the place. It was a pattern that circumstance had forced on the residents, but she could escape, and she wondered how and when she should. Every now and again someone would say something that made her realise that her presence was both pleasure and refreshment to one or other of them, and she felt deflected by this affection from her wish to move on, ashamed of it and at the same time alarmed at the prospect of being trapped.

One day, talking to Mary Carmichael as she helped her to bed, Mary said, "You know, it suddenly came over me. I remembered about our bodies changing all their cells, so that one is a different body every seven years, and I realised that if I met my husband again he might not know me. I'd be made of different material. It's just seven years since he died, so nothing that he knew is left of me. It kept me awake all night, it's a terrible thought. All of me gone, and yet still here. What do you make of it Lalla?"

When she told Tom this story an hour later as they were going to bed, his answer was simply that it was high time she left Marion's. Then, seeing how it had disturbed her, he said, "You must tell Francis. It's a poem for him to write."

"She felt that there was nothing left of her life with Chris Carmichael, no hand he had held, no kisses, nothing at all."

"Is it true anyway?" he wondered. "It sounds like some sort of folk lore." "That's often where truths get buried."

"It's a pity that we're not poets instead of researchers. But change of that sort is like water, rivers and waterfalls go on looking the same but it's always different water."

"Poor Mary," Lalla murmured, remembering that tired and sad face, "I'll tell her about waterfalls." She fell asleep with Tom's arm lying protectively across her shoulder.

When Maria told Charles that she was going away for a week with Alice, he asked,

"Because I'm here?"

"Yes."

"I thought that you liked having me here. It's not as if I was staying for long."

"I suppose I did like seeing you again, but I don't any more."

"Because I went to see Joanna's dragon of a mother?"

"Oh Charles, everything's wrong. That, and your clothes all over the flat, and 'where shall we go for dinner?'. It's all absolutely idiotic, and I can't bear it."

"But there's so much we ought to talk about."

"Nothing. Solicitors can do the talking."

"As you like. I went to the bank this morning."

"Yes?"

"Well, I think I've arranged things pretty well, and I'm getting my stuff collected at the end of the week to be shipped over. Do you want to stay here? I mean in this place?"

"Not really. It's been let too long to mean much. It's ages since we bought it."

"It's yours to sell, anyway, and I thought the usual arrangement about money."

"Can you afford that?"

"Of course. When are you and Alice going?"

"Tomorrow morning."

"So I shan't see you after this evening?"

"I suppose not." She did not want to go on talking about partings and endings, just wanting them to be over.

"Let's go to a film tonight."

"We could, why not?" This would fill up the evening, she supposed. So they did, but neither of them paid much attention to the screen, for both were wondering about the future.

Maria had packed a suitcase before she went to bed and she left the flat while Charles was still asleep. She found a taxi, and had breakfast at a café in Camden Town. She felt that seven o'clock was not the time to arrive at even such sympathetic friends as Alice and Francis's house. She spun out a couple of hours, reading 'The Times' and having many cups of coffee. At nine she paid her bill and found another taxi, for though the distance was minimal her suitcase seemed heavy, though she couldn't remember packing anything to make it so.

Alice was still in a dressing gown when she arrived.

"Goodness, is it as late as that?"

"No, I'm early. I hope you don't mind, I wanted to escape before Charles woke up."

"What about breakfast?"

"I've been drinking endless cups of Ness or something down the road." She looked very strained and tired.

"Well, come and sit down while I get dressed. I've been wondering about where you'd like to go."

"I suppose westwards. Shall we just go? I'm sure it will be easy to get places to stay at this time of year."

"There are maps and things on the table, shan't be long." Alice left her and went upstairs to dress. Maria found Lewis sleeping on the large volume of road maps. He lifted one eyelid, and then rolled over on his back and stretched. Maria accepted this invitation to admire him, and as she stroked him under his chin he started to purr. She picked him up, and, against his usual code of conduct, he relaxed against her shoulder and continued to purr. He seemed to have sensed her unhappiness and to be willing to be used as a comforting presence. Francis had heard Maria arrive, he'd been in his work room, and he had decided not to see Maria. He went, instead, to talk to Alice while she dressed.

"I hope it won't be too melancholy," he said.

"I couldn't see any way out of it." They had had practically the same conversation the night before, and Alice had made a list of people to whom he should telephone, things to cancel, and other domestic odds and ends. She promised to telephone about seven, and after last questions about money, keys and cheque books, he hugged her.

"Alice, I shall miss you dreadfully. I've just begun to realise how much."

"I know. But how I should hate it if you didn't."

He carried her suitcase down, then helped her load the car, carrying Maria's suitcase out from the hall. Then he went into the sitting room and found Maria crying quietly into Lewis's furry shoulder.

She put him onto the table and picked up the maps. "He has been nice to me", she said.

"My turn." Francis kissed Maria's cheek, and then offered his handkerchief.

"The car's ready. I filled it up yesterday, so you'll be all right for a bit. I expect you'll find somewhere interesting, and don't let Alice buy too many pretty jugs."

He waved to them as they drove away, and realised as he went indoors that the house felt quite different from the way it felt when he knew that Alice would be coming home at lunchtime or later in the day.

When Alice telephoned that evening she reported that they were at Rodborough, above Stroud. "We ambled rather, it's very golden, all those beechwoods and late sunshine."

"Are you alone?"

"Yes, telephone in my bedroom. I've taken off my shoes, and I brought a stiff drink upstairs. I'll meet Maria in the bar later. We'll dine here."

"How was it?"

"Confusing. She's half full of plans for the future, and half in tears and regrets and despairs. We did find one good junk shop, and that she enjoyed."

"What did you find?" Their trivialities were spoken in deeply affectionate voices.

"Oh, Francis, a perfectly lovely bowl, and two very pretty jugs, sort of Staffordshire stuff. One's pink, the other's apple green. It has a very little chip, but it's so pretty."

"Not a bad haul for your first day. If it goes on like this you'll come clanking back."

"I expect so. Cochineal and china dishes. Are the cats all right?"

"Of course, and, as you haven't asked, so am I. The house feels unnatural without you."

"So does this room without you. It's very comfortable and I expect that it has a lovely view. It was a bit dusky when we arrived."

"Must it be a whole week?"

"I don't know. I hope not. But if Charles is still in the flat it's not good coming back."

"Tell Maria to write and ask him to leave. He could drop the keys here. Then I'd know if he's gone."

"Yes. I'll ask her."

"You'll ring tomorrow?"

"Of course, of course. I do miss you."

"By the way, Stella has asked me to spend the evening with her tomorrow, so could you manage about six? Terence wants to go to a film and he won't if she'll be alone."

"He's a treasure. Yes, about six. I suppose I'd better stop now or the bill will be horrible."

"Oh Alice, I do miss you. Sorry to be repetitive, but I do."

"Goodnight my love, goodnight."

Alice put the telephone down reluctantly. She had been transported for the few minutes to London, to the room where Francis was sitting by the window, probably with Amy on his knee, certainly with a drink at hand. She was conscious of her security, and felt that it was extraordinary to think of Maria in her newly parted state, regretting and learning freedom. Then she thought with surprise that Francis hadn't sent his love to Maria.

Francis remembered it, too, as he put down the receiver. He remembered it the next day, when Alice reported that they were in Weymouth. She said that it was raining now and there wasn't a cinema, but that they had persuaded the hotel to cook mushrooms for them, that it had been a lovely day, and that they'd enjoyed themselves and were looking forward to dinner.

It hadn't started so well. After lunch, driving in through lanes, Maria had gone back to her worries. She had been talking about people she had known whose marriages had broken up, and who had re-married afterwards. "It's like those films about cells, or is it jellyfish? They break and make new shapes, and subdivide again, and go on for ever being in different patterns."

"Surely people don't often. . . " Alice saw Charles's arms and legs swimming off and becoming re-attached, like the three legs that represent, is it Sicily, she tried to remember, or the Isle of Man? Or lizards growing new tails, and lobsters growing fresh claws. She realised that Maria was looking at her, surprised.

"Natural history is bewildering," she said. "I was thinking of lizards."

"You are inconsequent. What on earth have lizards to do with divorces?"

"I'm sorry Maria, but you started the natural history bit."

"What I mean is that people seem to re-make their lives so casually when you look at it from the outside, and it is so different when it happens to oneself. I've seen at least four couples we knew fairly well, at one time or another, change partners, and it didn't look as if they were unhappy while it was going on, at least, not for long."

Would it be unsympathetic, or cheering, Alice wondered, to point out that Maria and Charles had not been in their parted, or should one call it pre-divorce, state for long? Before she said anything Maria went on.

"I don't suppose that I knew any of them very well, though I did see it coming on in one affair." They were silent for some minutes.

"Maria, what did you do all the time? You must have had a lot of time to fill up while Charles was at meetings or in an office or something. Were you lonely, or what did you do so as not to be?"

"Russian mostly. You know I've always enjoyed languages. I've what they call kept-up French, I've done some translation, and I review French novels when I'm asked to. It's been difficult sometimes, getting new ones to read unless I'm sent copies to review, so I felt a bit stick-in-the-muddish as I hadn't learnt anything new, so I started on Russian. It sounds so beautiful as one can usually find someone who can teach one wherever one is, and records, anyway. I can read it comfortably now."

"Goodness," said Alice. "You never talked about that with us."

"It never cropped up. It's not a secret vice, but it has kept me going. I'm not a creative person. I wish, most of all, that I'd been born a painter."

"Why? I know that it would be exciting, to be able to tell what you see so that everyone else could see it too."

Alice thought of the Dorset lanes they had driven through and the long curve of the Chesil beach they had seen from the top of the cliffs on Portland Bill, with a stormy, cloudy sunset over the sea.

"Much simpler than that. It would be so portable for a life like mine has been. I don't think there's anywhere we've been - " She had not yet learned to say 'I' instead of 'we' Alice noticed, sadly " - that there haven't been places to paint, or people. It must be marvellous to paint portraits, but I can't do anything like that. So, I learned Russian." She asked, "What about you?"

"Nothing that adds up to anything much."

Alice's life seemed very full to her as it happened. She and Francis had many friends, and this led to rather a lot of cooking, and that in turn to rather a lot of shopping, as well as to lively conversations. But that wasn't anything to talk about.

"I read a good deal, mostly history, and I do Francis's typing for him. He says that he thinks down his arm, and with his pen. Actually he's no good with anything as mechanical as a typewriter. It's why we don't own any indoor machinery, no washing up machine clattering our plates away. The typewriter is my mechanical limit."

"The lives we lead are self-indulgent, aren't they?" Maria said.

"Oh yes. I'm all for that. I find most days interesting, and independently so. I mean quite apart from Francis's work, which is always there, elation and despair, and new ideas, and new poems sometimes, but so many pleasures. Sometimes it's just things in the garden, or something someone says in the market, or something I read making sense of things I've wondered about. I'm all for self-indulgence."

"I remember, even when you were hard up, you always had lots of lace on petticoats, and flowers in the flat."

"So I did. So I do". A moment later, Alice said in an excited voice,

"Maria, I'm going to stop by the next gate. I think there are mushrooms in that field."

They were lucky, for a few yards further on a tiny track branched from the road.

They got out of the car. "If you're right, and I don't doubt you, Alice, what can we put them in? Have you got a carrier bag somewhere handy?"

"Hell, no I haven't," Then she brightened, "The junk shop jugs. They're in newspaper, and that's no good, so we'll have to use the jugs."

They walked back to the gate into the field where Alice thought she'd seen the mushrooms, each carrying a jug.

"Is it poaching?" Maria wondered. Neither of them were adept at country life and had no idea of what was permissible, but it seemed reasonable to suppose that if no one had claimed mushrooms by four o'clock in the afternoon, the owner of the field could not want them, and anyway, surely both mushrooms and blackberries were for the finders, whoever they were.

There were some, beautifully large, their gills still pinkish, and some tiny ones.

"Shall we pick the beginners as well as the big ones, do you think?" Maria asked.

"Oh yes, but do you suppose they'll cook them for us anywhere?" Alice had been so pleased with this treasure trove she'd forgotten about the next step. "I hadn't thought of that." Maria became very practical.

"If we don't pick too many we could probably find a good pull up for lorries and get them to do them with eggs and bacon for lunch tomorrow."

"Or if we get a lot, both jugs full, we could give them some extra ones?"

"Why not? I haven't found mushrooms since I was about eight."

"I don't think they grow in many places now, I suppose this is such a steep field no one has bothered with fertilizer or anything."

Both jugs full, they scrambled downhill.

"Wrong sort of shoes we're wearing."

"Never mind. I tell you what, Maria, we'll go blackberrying on our way home, as well. Look there are lots in these hedges."

There were, as well as briony, a few tiny green flowers left, though the leaves were yellowing, and the berries ripening to bright clusters on the trailing stalks winding among the already cloudy seedheads of old man's beard.

They put the full jugs on the floor at the back of the car.

"Simple pleasures, as you were saying." Maria was looking happy for the moment.

"Acquisitiveness, greed, probably theft, treasure hunting, absolutely marvellous," Alice agreed as they drove on.

Of course Alice did not go into all this story; Francis heard by her tone of voice that it had been a good day. Alice, he thought, is getting something out of it all, and he remembered this time to send love to Maria before Alice rang off.

He felt much more cheerful as he set out to see Stella. He bought a bottle of whisky on his way, and from a shop on Primrose Hill that was closing late, a pot of yellow lilies.

Stella was pleased to see him. She had had a bottle of champagne put in the fridge, and Terence opened it for them, refused to drink with them, and spun off into the evening looking very carefree.

Francis poured out second glasses, and sat down in a more comfortable chair than he had started with.

"I'm starved for talk, Francis."

"Terence?"

"Oh yes, he's a love, and amusing, and in a sort of way having a man about the place is comfortable. But he's so young. No cross-references, I feel as old as I am, and he's a grandchild's age. Talk to me of death, Francis."

"Why death, Stella?"

"I've got to contemplate it. I don't mean overdoses and all that, though of course I've got my little pamphlet tucked away. But I suppose I'm on the brink of the void and no one will talk about it. In the Home," she gave a sideways look at him and saw that he had reacted by raising an eyebrow, "oh yes, I'm being bitchy, but I can be with you, it was incontinence and library books and smoothing everything over, and let today be got through to the Mogadon hour. It wasn't bearable. Those dropped bosoms and withered everything. Well, no, I didn't actually see them, but withered I'm sure they are, and nothing about what we're all facing, being extinguished uncomfortably."

"It must be extraordinary for people who are believers in a future life," Francis said. "Some of the ideas are so beguiling, the meadows on the top of Mount Purgatory with all the heathen poets strolling about gossiping, and I suppose all their lovers too. And Jerusalem, my happy home, with the gardens and the gallant walks. But, when it comes to it, does it matter? It'll either be something unimaginable or just like sleep, when one goes off into nothingness."

"It's clinging to oneself, isn't it? More champagne? I told Terence to put another bottle in the fridge."

"Lots in this one still," Francis refilled their glasses.

"Yes," he said, "of course it's that. Identity is about the only thing about which I feel entirely possessive. I hate the thought of letting it go. But, Stella, we've had fortunate lives because we've been able to do the things we want to do, and get paid for doing them."

"Not much. I've got an overdraft again, but of course it doesn't matter," she added hastily, "there'll be some P.R.S. and I never pay the rates till I get one of those final-final notices so I needn't count that."

Francis remembered that she had told him, long ago, when she was in debt she always bought champagne. He thought that she always bought it anyway, so it wasn't only a distress signal.

"How is Alice getting on with that frightful man's wife?"

"Hard to say. She telephones rather geographically. They're drifting round the West Country. Maria seems to be in a state of shock, mostly I think from realising that she hadn't realised how thin their marriage had become, but Alice was much more cheerful this evening. They'd been mushrooming."

"Well, don't get entangled yourself. Unattached, recently unattached, women always need reassurance, and a sudden no-sex life is rotten for the morale, so she's probably dangerous. I told Alice to be careful weeks ago, when she came back."

"Did you, now? Alice didn't tell me that."

"I don't suppose that she tells you everything."

"No. Why should she?"

"And I suppose you don't tell her everything, either."

"Telling, telling. You don't talk about the work you're doing, except in a general way, do you? It has to be put into its medium, into its shape, hasn't it, before it can be spoken about to anyone."

"How have you two managed to stay married for so long, anyway? You're both intelligent and lively and yet, there you are, sitting about together, going everywhere together, holidays and all. Don't you get bored? Don't you know each other too well?"

"Haven't you ever wanted to be with any of the people in your life for ever?"

Francis parried her question. He was damned if he was going to discuss Alice with her.

"Not since I was about twenty," she answered. "I don't know why, except that I got bored. No one kept my imagination alive for long. Five years, I suppose, was the longest. And I like solitude to a degree, but I like it mixed with excitement, and I don't like, God how I don't like, sleeping alone. It's a waste of time, not having a lover."

"It sounds to me," Francis said, "that you've not been lucky. You should have had a Medici prince at least."

"That, of course, is a pleasant and flattering thought, but I doubt if they were as good as they were cracked up to be. Is anybody? Was anybody? So one leaves life unsatisfied by what it has had to offer, unsatisfied with one's own work, well, generally unsatisfied."

"Better than being complacent and grateful for small mercies."

"Of course. Steer for the deep waters only."

Then, abruptly changing the subject, she asked, "What's Lalla up to?"

"Looking for a job. I think she's had enough of Marion's."

"So, I suppose this research work is a sort of tribute to her grandparents?"

"Oh it all started when she and Tom found an old boy who'd had a fall, and took him to hospital. But, you may be right, it may be wanting to do something positive for the old because she was, she told us, absolutely devoted to her grandparents."

"The Home must have been a disillusioning experience, all in all."

"No, I don't think so. You're a bleak realist, and she's still young enough to believe that things can be put right by personal effort and by compassion."

"She certainly cheered me while I was there. And Tom?"

"Good hearted, finding his way, very much in love with her."

"Lucky to be so young, unlucky to live in these times."

"Yes and no. What about that smoked salmon. Are you ready for supper?"

"I am, I am. But you'll have to cope. Terence, I hope, has left everything for you."

He had. There was a plate of brown bread and butter, sliced lemon with the salmon, and a tray arranged with a bowl of peaches and pears.

"Shall I cut it up? Or can you manage?"

"Help would be acceptable." Stella's hands were hurting her and holding a fork was none too easy, but a knife was impossible. Francis made minute sandwiches for her, and later peeled a peach, and then made coffee. They finished the second bottle of champagne having a surprisingly cheerful talk about the frightfulness of nature, the elegance of the food chain and the obvious lack of compassion in what or whoever had created such complicated processes. Francis, rather to his surprise, found himself telling Stella of his dream about the dark and desert plain and the ramparts beyond, and the feeling of liberation and joy he had felt.

"The myths die hard, don't they?" she said. "It must have been interesting to lose one's faith, a hazard no one has to face nowadays as they don't have any. A good subject for novelists lost for ever."

"We have detective stories now. They're getting bloodier and nastier." Stella said that all the same she enjoyed them. Francis said that he did not. The conversation drifted on, and returned to the subject of overdrafts. She was looking tired.

"What time is Terence coming home?" Francis was concerned.

"Any time now. He's between lovers, and I suppose questing around. But tonight he was going out with a couple of friends to a film at the Curzon. I expect they'll have a drink or some supper after."

As she spoke Terence arrived and Stella dismissed Francis.

"Lovely evening, come again soon," she said. "Terence, put me to bed. I don't think that I can get across the room. Francis, you give me an arm too"

Between them they half carried her to her room. "Can you manage?"

Terence nodded, and Stella said, "Yes, yes he's used to it. Go along now, Francis."

So Francis walked home through a cold autumn breeze, wondering how Terence felt about undressing Stella, and how she felt about his ministrations, which he imagined would have to be both intimate and impersonal.

Francis and Alice had spent so very little time apart during their married lives that a letter from Alice was a surprise, particularly as she had managed to telephone to him every evening.

The weather had changed again, and the day was serene, golden, echoing the first touches of yellow in the lime trees further down the street. It seemed to have reached Dorset a day or two before, for

Alice wrote:

"It's rather a luxury, having time to write to you after goodness-knows how long. Maria has a headache, and so I've a whole evening to myself. And how better to spend it than in writing to you? We went to Corfe today; bright sunshine and lots of gossamer floating about, ragwort of course, and little blue scabious, both early autumn colours, and a few red leaves on bushes of the wayfarer's tree, which isn't a tree and bryony flowers and berries together. Enough; it is such an entrancing village, but the castle seems to me powerfully horrible, a brooding, doom-laden evil place. This is strange, for I haven't had that sort of feeling about other ruins, or only slightly so and most of them must have been filled with murders, and awful sieges, but mostly all that seems to have blown away. Grass in the courtyards, valerian on the walls. Little notices about what was where, and Ladies and Gents accommodation are very purging. Or perhaps I am picking up Maria's moods? At the moment she's lost all self-confidence. Is it possible to live with an *idea* of the person you live with, an image of what they ought to be in your life? I'd say that is roughly what she sees she has been doing for years. Anyway, my prescription for her restoration is a lot of new admirers *and* a lover. She needs to be in bloom to be herself, and she's considerably wilted. She talks a great deal, but it's getting nowhere new. I'm dying to come home. Darling Francis, I hate sleeping alone, I hate waking up in all these different rooms by myself, and longing to talk to you. It has made me think of all the people at Marion's, all the old people in single beds, who know that there is no more touch, no more pillow talk, no more pleasure in being together. Of course I'm not forgetting the ones like the Hacketts for whom a shared room is a sentence, and must have been for years. But this week has gone on and on and on, and I grasp at our moments on the telephone as a life line, and I tell you, clearly and finally, Francis, I will *not* be left a widow, so please, please remember this. Darling, I'm becoming maudlin, I cried as I wrote that, I think I'd better stop and look at the ten o'clock news, then go to bed. If I was alone for long I'd certainly follow in Stella's footsteps and take to the bottle. I have got some delicious nightcap; a bedroom fridge is a great comfort to a grass widow. It is golden weather. I shall insist on a day by the sea, on a beach, with rock pools, and I trust to hear from you, as soon as

407

possible, that Charles has cleared out of the flat. When I know the coast is clear and I can plan to come home, will you be an angel and stock up M.'s fridge with something? Smoked salmon perhaps and bread and butter, and a bunch of something cheerful? Sorry to bother you, and ten thousand questions to ask about Stella and Lalla and the cats. Love - all I have - Alice.

"I've sent postcards to Stella, and to Marion's and to Lalla and Tom. I feel as if I've been in exile for months."

"And I think I begin to guess what being banished was like. That awful speech in "Richard II". I always *liked* Norfolk. And that moment when he knows he will be cut off from the language, as well as the places, total homesickness, 'shades of endless night...' I hope that my banishment from you will end soon, even another three days feels pretty endless."

Francis wanted to write to her at once, but not knowing where to send a letter settled that idea. Instead, he telephoned to Charles, and agreed to meet him for lunch to receive the keys of the flat. All business had been completed, Charles said, and he'd be flying at the weekend. Meanwhile he would move into 'quite a comfortable hotel'. "Living alone in the flat is hopeless," he said. Charles continued in such an attitude when they met. He had developed, Francis thought, an amazing self-centredness, or perhaps it had become his most visible characteristic. It had, inevitably, made him boring. Of Maria he did not speak, except to say that he would have no chance to say goodbye before he left. Francis was tempted to say that she probably would not wish to say that, or anything else to him. He accepted the keys, and went home.

One effect of Alice's being away was to make him work very late. His old-age poems were exciting him. He was living in an euphoric state, and almost enjoying what Alice was so desperately missing. Though, he thought, everything is much better when there's work, and it's much easier being alone among familiar things. He noticed with pleasure, when he re-read her letter, that she was not fussing about his comforts, and that she took for granted the housekeeping for the cats.

Both cats took advantage of Alice's absence to sleep with him, Lewis on Alice's pillow, and Amy on his feet.

Alice telephoned at nine on the day her letter had come.

"Any news?"

"Your letter - bless you. Yes, and news. Charles has left the flat. We had lunch at a pub and I have the keys. It was a horrid lunch, but I have done what you told me. I bought extravagant quantities of smoked salmon - it seems the answer to everything - enough for us all."

"Does that mean you and the cats, or you and me, tomorrow?"

"Well, both. We had some tonight."

"Oh Francis, not the cats?"

"I gave them a very little. Self defence."

Alice laughed. "I'll have to feed you on pasta and cabbage to settle the housekeeping."

"That you won't. What time will you arrive?"

"'Tea time, at a guess. Then I can take Maria back to the flat."

"Is she all right?"

"No. But I think she'll be better in London, and finding something to do."

"Alone?"

"I know. But it has got to be faced."

"Drive carefully love, I want you home in one piece."

"Yes. When do I not drive carefully?"

"I won't tell Stella or anyone that you're coming home, not till after the weekend."

"I was going to suggest that. Tomorrow then."

"Tomorrow. Goodnight Alice, sleep well."

"Better, tomorrow."

It was still good weather, a sunny day, very still. In the morning Francis picked a bunch of late roses, some dark pansies, and a few, discreetly cut, tobacco flowers and put them in one of Alice's favourite jugs, arranged tea things on a tray so that they could have tea in the garden, and then worked till lunch time. After some bread and cheese he worked all through the afternoon and, to his surprise, forgot about time till he heard the car stopping at the gate. It was nearly five he noticed. He hurried to the door and down the path to the gate.

Alice was just getting out of the car, Maria undoing her seat belt, as she heard his voice. Though he only spoke Alice's name, Maria realised how much he must have missed his wife, how unshakeable an affection there was between them, although she could not see the looks in their eyes, only their hands meeting, from where she sat.

Francis unloaded Alice's suitcase from the boot.

"Goodness," he said. "Are all those carrier bags...?"

"Yes," said Alice. "We found some very good junk shops. We'll have to be careful. Junk shops of the right kind never have enough paper to wrap things properly."

"All yours?"

Maria, by now out of the car, said, "I couldn't restrain her, Francis. She says that it's her Christmas shopping. And there are some blackberries, we bought boxes to put them in."

Francis kissed Maria, and she helped to carry in the treasures.

After tea Maria said that she should go back to her flat. There was a moment's hesitation about which of them should drive her, then Alice said that she would like to unpack, so it was Francis who took her home, carried up her luggage, and gave her the keys.

"Why - you've been in and put flowers for me. How lovely."

"Alice said that you would probably like smoked salmon, so there's some brown bread and some butter in the fridge, and a lemon, and a bottle."

"Thank you. Alice has been an angel, and it was marvellous to be away from all this."

Charles had, at least, left the place tidy and, he had told Francis, that their help had been in, and had made the bed and done the laundry, so the flat, except for the tall vase of tiger lilies, looked as if it had been long uninhabited.

"Will you be all right?"

"Of course." Maria was making an effort to be calm.

"We'll meet soon." He was longing to go home, and she saw this.

"You've been an angel too, sparing Alice."

"Oh, she's her own woman," he said, and then, establishing something, instinctively self-protective he thought, as he drove home, he had said, "We are your friends, Maria."

Chapter 8

Lalla's three day week had, somehow, become a four day week at Marion's. It still gave her a long free weekend, and most evenings. She and Tom had been at work assembling, correlating and ordering their work. Now it was typed, and both of them were rather nervous about it as well as relieved. They had made several photocopies. Tom took one to Alice and Francis, and Lalla asked Mrs. Miles to read another. After ten days of saying nothing, and Lalla knew, of course, how busy she was, Mrs. Miles asked Lalla to come to her sitting room for tea. Lalla was nervous about that all through the day, which was a particularly busy one. Wednesday was the doctor's day. Also various appointments had to be made with the visiting hairdresser, and her clients fetched from bedroom or the main sitting room at appropriate times, as well as some small shopping commissions done; Minette's daily walk was mostly round the shops, with an extra twenty minutes off the lead on Primrose Hill, a rather sedate exploration of tree boles and what might be described as a leisurely stroll on the grass beside the path rather than the officially used words 'a good run'. Her running days were as lost as her figure. Lalla was glad of her company, all the same, as she finished the shopping and took her there. A sharp breeze was blowing down the first of the autumn leaves, mostly chestnut leaves, yellowy edges to each spoke of the fan, and a few of the smaller ones were bowling along the paths. Minette's waddle became livelier as she chased them, and both Lalla and she were soon out of breath.

"Come on, Minette, tea time, and you've nothing to face, as I have." She talked to her, all the way back to the house, but Minette paid little attention to her words.

Mrs. Miles said, "Come in Lalla, dear." She was smiling, and Lalla's apprehensions vanished.

"I'm sorry that I've taken so long over reading your work, but you know what my days are like, and I have had a couple of bad nights looking after Henry. He's getting very fragile I'm afraid."

"I know. I've noticed that he's not so full of gossip as he used to be, it's sad."

"Sit down, my dear. You don't have milk in your tea, do you?"

"Thank you." Lalla took the cup and saucer and, amused and touched, a Jaffa cake.

Mrs. Miles laughed. "I know. We all like them, and you at least don't have to worry about weight. Now - I'm impressed. I was rather anxious about using us, even as a background to Dame Stella, but you've been both tactful and discreet, and of course I was amused by some of your character sketches. I like the way you have used first-name initials rather than anything else, but I'm going to suggest that you change even those. What about using their second name initials. Henry's other name is Leonard, perhaps you knew? Anyway, that's a minor problem. You have managed to let so much shine out. The difficulties overcome, the settling, sometimes for so little, and the background of the physical problems which can so often be all that anyone less sensitive can see."

"Goodness," said Lalla. "And I was terrified about what you'd think."

"Why?"

"Well, you know so much about them all. I keep reminding myself that Alice told me that this place was about courage. When I see all those loads of sheets going into the laundry room, and the rows of bottles and pills, and all the other impedimenta..."

"Yes. And in hospitals, of which you probably know little, there's always the cheerful side - people leaving better than they came in, of mending, as it were. Here, it's making, trying to make-do, with never being able to see that; but where there's life, there must be some pleasure and every comfort we can give. Of course, this is a picnic compared with places that haven't all our resources. Money, I'm afraid, but as it's there for a set purpose, it's wonderful to be able to use it."

"You do it so well."

"It's all of us. I liked your other star performer, F."

"You *would* like Fred, he's tough and real."

"He comes over."

Lalla put her cup down carefully and got up and went to kiss Mrs. Miles, who blushed with surprise - with realisation of Lalla's appreciation.

"Now," she said, "more tea? And we'll talk about Dame Stella."

"Yes."

"You know, you've worked it out well. Fred and Stella, the lion and the unicorn I think. The countryman, an almost extinct species, though I can just remember people like that when I was a child, and the extraordinary - which she was to me - I've not met those sort of creative people much; for the ones here, now, aren't in the same world."

"I feel lucky to know her."

"Yes. She was rather startling at first, but she was so stimulating, though I was angry with her much of the time. It's funny, really, liking, admiring and being furious all at once."

"I do miss her," Lalla said.

"So do I. And I never expected to."

"You've been to see her in her flat?"

"Oh yes. She asked me round for a drink three days ago. It was amazing to see her so, not domestic exactly, among her own possessions. But Terence is exactly right for her. He's so kind."

"I like him too. He's unexpected, isn't he?"

"He's having a fine time. He seems to love meeting her friends. They'd had some of her students to lunch, and some famous American composer had been there, another one was coming today I think. Anyway, she thrives on his cooking. I had worried about that, for I gather she had thought she'd survive on meals on wheels and..."

"Whisky?" Lalla finished.

Mrs. Miles said, "Yes. Now, there is one other thing, Lalla. Have you and Tom shown this to Alice? She's Chairman of our Committee, and though we have Trustees and a Treasurer for all that side of the business, I think she may feel that she ought to bring this up at a Committee meeting."

Seeing Lalla's surprise, she went on, "No need to ask permission. You've been, as I said, so discreet, but as a matter of courtesy. And as you are still, thank goodness, an employee here. You see?"

"I hadn't thought of that. Yes, of course. And the Dulacs have a copy, too, so of course she knows."

"That's all right then. I expect Alice will be here tomorrow. There are some things we have to talk about. So we can add this to the list."

She got up and crossed to her desk and got out the blue folder.

"You've done well by us all. I like the thought of people as young as you are seeing so much, and not being patronising."

416

"But how could we be?"

"There's a tendency to think that no group of people from another age are as real as your own."

"Thank you, and for tea." Lalla knew that she was being dismissed.

"Thank you, my dear. I shall miss you when you move on, as you must. I hope that it won't be too soon though."

"I *have* learned so much from you. I shan't forget any of it, I hope."

"We have been paying each other compliments," Mrs. Miles looked at her watch. "Now, you must go home, and I shall go and see how Henry is doing."

Lalla walked home thinking about Mrs. Miles. "Perhaps we should write about the lookers-after?" she said to Tom when she told him about her afternoon. "I suppose they like it, but my goodness, all the part I couldn't face, the mechanics; you know, the actual nursing bits, the clearing-up, the bedpans," she shuddered. "That's, to me, the amazing thing. She could never, absolutely never, be a granny-basher, and I have seen how easily I could."

"You, Lalla?" Tom sounded horrified.

"I hope not, but sometimes, the slowness, the clumsiness. But she, and so many others, can see beyond that; beyond that shuffle and mumble, and know a real person that I can't always see, and would lose so easily if I had to cope every day. And she's so pretty, and all those different geraniums. Touching those, dead-heading them, that's so normal. The other things, and all the patience, and being so capable."

"Well Lalla, you can write that one, if you want to, but it's not for me."

Tom had delivered a copy of their work to Alice, and both she and Francis had read it.

"It's an interesting episode, I think," Francis said.

"In their lives?"

"Yes. I think they've done well. Two figures of equal age, astonishingly different. They've caught the tone of voice, and a tapestry of other people as a backcloth."

"I thought that too." Alice was a little worried that Stella might be recognised, and might not like it.

"Most unlikely. The people who will read this aren't the sort of people who'd be likely to know or pursue her music; she's a minority pleasure. And anyway, all publicity is good publicity. Marion's comes over immensely well."

"So we give our blessing? I shall have to tell the Committee about it, but I think they'll be pleased rather than anxious."

"Anyway, what emerges is a study of two people, in age; yes, but undefeated, perhaps a cheering matter for others already old, getting old?"

"And I hope a success for them, a beginning?"

Lalla was more nervous when she showed their work to Stella. Her verdict was one of amusement.

"Warts and all," she said. "I can't imagine who'll want to read it. I like your Fred, though, I wish we'd had him as an inmate, it would have been far more fun than all those stick-in-the-muds that I was rude to."

Terence said that he'd read it, too, and enjoyed it. "Not that that's anything to go by, but I thought you'd like to know."

"Is this your swan song as guardian angel, Lalla? I should think that it's time you closed that chapter and moved on to something jollier."

"I know, but I am in confusion about what I should do. The thing is, that I can't think how poor Minette will survive without me. The people will, but I do think that it's awful to abandon animals."

"She won't be abandoned. It's not as if she didn't get food and water. She'll probably have a heart attack a bit sooner than otherwise. So don't be so sentimental, Lalla."

"Is she very old?" Terence asked.

"I think she's about twelve. Old for her breed."

"Well, you shouldn't sit around waiting for her to die."

"Terence has a lot of sense," said Stella.

Chapter 9

"It's now or never," Francis said to Alice, "that is if you want to swim without having to go to some utterly distant place which we can't afford anyway."

"Now, then. It's been such a peculiar year with so much happening."

"Other people's happenings. It's quite time for you to do something you want to do. I would like to go away from all of them, even if it's for a fortnight."

"Stella's all right, Charles has gone, nothing to keep us."

"When I was out this morning I collected some leaflets and so forth. I discover that we could go to Cyprus any time next week. It's still hot, the sea will be warm, and we can hire a car and explore."

"Next week? Well yes, why not?" Alice felt excited, pleased, and wondered about clothes in one breath.

"Look." Francis gave her a couple of brochures, and they sat down together and gazed at improbable seas and white beaches, hotels that looked unnecessarily horrible, hopelessly large, or self-catering villas which, as Alice said, were her idea of a non-holiday.

"Well - this one?"

She had reached Kyrenia, the castle and the cypruses at Bella Pais, and there was another hotel, an old fashioned building and right on the sea, that looked to her more agreeable.

"Wherever we go is chancing our luck; we've left it so late, but this looks possible. Shall we try?" he asked.

"Thank goodness you're resourceful. I'd have gone on with wishful thinking, I suppose."

They discussed the next things, and the most important, who would look after the house and the cats.

"Maria," Alice suggested. "She can manage very well, and it would make a change for her."

"Any other suggestions?"

"No one else available as far as I can think. I don't want to have to put the cats in clink again, though they don't seem to mind."

"Too expensive if avoidable," Francis agreed. "Try her tomorrow."

Maria was delighted. She had not done more than write a note to Alice about their escape, thanking her, saying that she felt much better and very glad to have missed seeing Charles again. "I'll come round for instructions. When would you like me to move in?"

"Francis is getting tickets today. He's bustling around travel agents and all that. I think flights are twice a week."

"Will you stop in Istanbul?"

"Istanbul? Oh, that sounds wonderful. I hadn't realised that was a possibility, is it?"

"I should think so. How long will you be away?"

"Two weeks I suppose. It'll be some sort of package arrangement, as we've left it so late I doubt it will be possible to do anything special so, probably not. I'll tell you tomorrow what Francis has fixed, and then we can make all the arrangements. You are sure you don't mind?"

"Actually delighted. I'll be glad not to be here; I am going to move and so I can go on with the house-hunting while you're away."

Alice arranged to go to Marion's later in the day, and told Francis that she might be out to lunch.

"There's some soup in the fridge, and lots of cheese, if you get back in time."

"Fine. Don't let them bully you into doing anything you don't want to do."

Alice went shopping. She found a pair of lime green sandals, a pink cotton skirt, chose half a dozen paperback novels, some new sun glasses, two tubes of anti-sunburn cream, and a couple of short-sleeved shirts for Francis as a surprise present, one deep blue, one coppery red. Loaded with her carrier bags, and full of pleasure at her success, she arrived at Marion's.

"Meg," she said to Mrs. Miles. "I've been gloriously indulgent. Can you give me some tea and tell me all the news."

"Good news first. Henry's better and on his feet again. He was very sorry for himself all last week and I was worried about him. One evening he gave a very good imitation of a deathbed scene. He asked me to forgive him for all the magazines I should find in his cupboard."

"Girlie mags?"

"Oh yes, and some pretty pornographic ones, too. I knew about them, one of the girls had seen them lying about when she did his room. I suppose that he puts them away, usually, before he goes downstairs. She was rather upset."

"What did you do?"

"Told her that what the Residents read was not our business and tried to explain that for some of the old men it was a sort of compensation for not having girlfriends."

"Then?"

"Well, it came out that her uncle is a very "Page Three" man, and her mother says it's disgusting and that he ought to know better. So I had a little talk with her, and suggested that if she ever found them again she should leave them as he had left them. She's a bright girl, our Tracey, and she understood very quickly. She was upset, I think, because she's always admired Henry."

"What did you say to him?"

"That it might be a good idea for me to get rid of the ones he's finished with, for him. I don't like cupboards full of old paper, anyway. He was very touching about it all."

"He's really better?"

"Quite all right again."

"The bad news?"

"I've been worried about Mary Carmichael. She's getting very vague, I'm afraid that her memory is blurring everything, and she realises it. Keeps apologising for being so stupid. She minds so much."

"Do you need more help for her?"

"Not yet. Someone helps her to dress, and fetches her for meals. Don't you worry about anything Alice, go and enjoy yourself. Everything is under control. Tell me about your shopping."

Francis had also had a successful day. A room looking over the sea in the hotel that they had thought the most promising, in Kyrenia, a flight on the following Tuesday. It was Friday now; a new pair of bathing trunks, and a new zip bag with a shoulder strap "for bathing things and all that," he said, "and for the flight."

They spread out their shopping and admired their day's work. Francis was delighted with his shirts and said he had thought about buying new ones, but all he had seen had been horrible colours.

"Did you talk about Lalla and Tom's book?"

"At the very last moment. I was so elated with my shopping I almost forgot, and there was a lot of stuff about Henry being ill and porn magazines. Meg does deal with all that sort of thing with so much sense."

"And?"

"Oh, she said that it ought to be called 'The Lion and the Unicorn'. Do you think that Stella would like to be called the unicorn?"

"Wouldn't mind at all, I should think, it's a special creature, mythical, beautiful, romantic, stands for magical and noble qualities. Not, as you might say, unflattering,"

"Lalla loves Fred. She and Tom have done a good job if they've managed to make all of us want to meet Fred."

"I wonder if we shall? I doubt it. He may be better as a story - for all of us." Francis was beginning to be bored by the subject, but he was fair.

"They haven't romanticized Stella, so they've probably been just as accurate about Fred. The remarkable thing is their generous understanding."

"Yes," she said. What she felt was a need of a holiday from other people's lives. Stella had been a responsibility, but one no longer hers. She'd organised stepping-stones, as it were, and for a time, at any rate, Stella had regained the independence she needed. Maria had been a difficult problem. Alice had been more surprised by the fact that she'd been working and learning Russian than by the break up of her marriage. She felt ashamed of having underestimated Maria and she was dismayed to have done so. It was quite a time before she could bring herself to tell Francis about it. She was grateful for his reaction.

"Of course she had to do something, and how sensible of her. It means that she'll be able to find interesting work to do. She's, in any case, not going to starve, and this is a part of her life that has nothing to do with Charles, so it will be a continuity."

Actually, he was very relieved to learn of these activities, for they showed that Maria had more strength of purpose than she'd shown through all the last weeks.

"You've had too many burdens. It has been hard going, hasn't it? But I don't think that either Stella or Maria could have managed without you. You're an amazing creature, Alice, it never ceases to surprise me how you manage to spend so much time and imagination on other people and yet to go on being uncorrupted by the sort of power you have."

"Good heavens, Francis, and I was feeling ashamed of myself for being so glad to be away from them all." She was surprised by his words.

"Perhaps you should think of them standing on their own feet now, and then absolutely forget them all and live for pleasure. You're very good at that and it's a considerable talent."

****

He looked at her, already faintly sunburned, with pleasure and amusement. It was Henry James again, on the table beside her.

"Thank goodness we're here. What a journey," she said.

They were having a very late breakfast on a terrace overlooking the sea. It wasn't a bedroom terrace, but one where blueish tablecloths and white furniture looked cool, and which was shaded by small feathery trees in tubs. The sea was pale this morning, and silky. Francis had been for a swim in the deep water by the little breakwater, where sunbathers were already lying on long white chairs. His hair was still damp, which somehow made him look young.

"Coffee good, honey marvellous, toast, no marks at all," he said, "but I don't care."

"Grapes, wonderful," Alice added.

They had arrived very late after a complicated change at Istanbul airport, where no one seemed to have exact information about which door led to the particular area of tarmac where they had to go to identify their baggage before it was reloaded. Both of them were shocked by the number of soldiers with guns, at both Istanbul and the Cyprus airport, and by the lack of directions, queues and other orderly arrangements. But the car from the hotel had been there to meet them and though the drive was longer than they had expected, Cyprus brandy and some rather half-hearted-looking sandwiches had revived them enough to unpack a little before they fell into bed. Now, a fortnight lay before them, clear and untroubled as the sea.

"I'll go and see about hiring a car. One can do it at the office here. Then a map, and we'll go exploring."

"Wonderful. I'll go and collect our bathing things. Shall we take books?"

"Might as well, and those cane mats. We'll probably find a sandy beach somewhere."

This they did find, and a tiny taverna where they lunched on grilled fish with salad, and country bread, iced beer and sweet coffee. They found some shade too, at the edge of the sand, and slept for an hour.

Spreading Ambre Solaire on her legs, which were far too pale for her satisfaction, Alice said, reverting, really unable to escape from her friends, "That was an odd telephone call from Stella."

"Yes. Well, I suppose she still feels a bit lost if she knows you aren't ten minutes away."

"It wasn't quite like an ordinary 'have a lovely time' goodbye, though."

"I think she's very much aware of what you've done for her all through the summer."

"It was a great declaration of friendship and how much it means, as well as about the pleasure of knowing a decent poet."

"Good references for us both." Francis lit a cigarette, and stood up. "I don't think that she'll die, but if she does, if she should not be there when we get home, we'll all be glad she said so much to you. And good too, for her to have said it. Now, shall we walk along the beach before we have another swim?"

"Why not. I wonder if there are any shells on this sort of beach. It doesn't look like a shell beach, so far. Still, you never know."

After another bathe they drove back to the town.

"We must go to the castle sometime, and up into the hills. I expect there's an awful lot to see, but I don't feel like doing anything much."

"We could go and have a drink by the harbour?"

"I don't consider that is doing anything much, so yes, of course. I suppose we might as well have dinner at the hotel tonight?"

The days passed most pleasantly. The tiny town was soon explored. Sometimes they dined by the harbour, little restaurants almost joined each other round the curving edge; on one side the solid, yellowish, stone castle commanded the narrow entrance to the basin, on the other the town was a jumble of houses and roofs, palm trees and a tower or two. Yachts were moored all along the water's edge, and the customs house came alive with excited crowds whenever packet boats from Turkey left or arrived. There was a smell of fish, diesel oil, cooking, and sea. And for both Alice and Francis a most comfortable lack of hurry, no plans, no decisions beyond the choice of a place to bathe, a place to see, or where to have a drink, a dinner, or, occasionally, a picnic. Alice found the choice of postcards so limited that she decided to send very few. Postcards had become a ridiculous holiday task, she felt, and why should she send them because other people had favoured them with exotic and glossy views of Bangkok or Les Baux? So, one for Maria, one for Stella, one for Mrs. Morris who came to do housework for them, one for Mrs. Miles, and a general greeting for the Residents. Even these occupied a morning on a rocky beach. Francis took them up to the Post Office for her.

"The stamps are pretty here," he said when he came back, "all flowers. And, most extraordinary, there's a tree outside the Post Office covered with advertisements, some in a glass case, but most of them pinned on to the tree. There's a concert in the castle on Saturday. Shall we go?"

"What sort of a concert?"

"That is undisclosed. It starts at eight thirty."

"It might be fun. Yes. Where do we get tickets?"

"At the door. The castle is so huge there won't be any problem about getting in."

The concert had obviously been arranged to coincide with a full moon. The lighting arrangements other than this natural effect were scant, and the stage lights had cables trailing about the great courtyard. The seating was a collection of chairs of all sorts. Alice had a wooden folding chair, Francis, next to her, a bentwood one with a cane seat which had seen better days. The audience was of all ages from infants in arms to ancient men and women who looked as uncomfortable as it is possible to be in pursuit of pleasure, as most of the seats were vastly smaller than the people they accommodated. There were many children, some wandered about, but they were all quiet and good-mannered if not absorbed by the performance. Some of them went to sleep, as did the one next to Francis, and leant heavily against his shoulder.

The first item was three dancers, in very pink body stockings and little else, who did some acrobatic dashing about. The man occasionally lifted one of the girls from an arabesque on his right to another she achieved as he put her down on his left. Next a choir, very neatly dressed in white shirts and black skirts or trousers, with a very young conductor. They sang well, music that might have been by Kodály, but was, as Alice thought, more probably 'school of'. Then the dancers again, now in green tunics, then more by the choir. Then an interval in which Alice and Francis had time to look around. The castle, even in its rundown state, was immensely grand and vast, big enough to have held a substantial army or a large population sheltering from a siege (they had, as yet, not read a guide book). The second half of the concert was surprisingly filled by a modestly good performance of Bach's 'The Coffee Cantata'; the orchestra was better than the singers, and though, as Francis said, it couldn't have been a more unlikely setting for the action - the singers were in full eighteenth-century dress - they enjoyed themselves.

Next day they went back to the castle and looked at the little ship museum, the earliest known shipwreck, four lost sailors, the only trace of their lives four little plates and four spoons, their cargo of amphorae from several islands, and a ballast of millstones.

"Archaeology makes me melancholy."

"Well, do you want to go up to the other castle, or has this been enough for you?" Alice sighed, her sandals were hurting.

"Enough for today. Let's go somewhere and swim, and then perhaps the other one tomorrow?"

"Only four more days. Yes, we'd better go there tomorrow."

When Francis thought about that Cyprus holiday, the things he remembered were all to do with sea: the four cyprus trees in the courtyard at Bella Pais, and the sheltering hills behind the abbey, the sea to the north, a flat clear calm; the wider stretch visible from the upper ward of St. Hilarion's Castle, a hot, steep climb which Alice had decided against for herself, preferring ice cold but otherwise nasty fizzy lemonade on the balcony of the roofed room where that and such things as postcards and sweets were for sale. She said that she had climbed far enough. Francis scrambled up to the very top buildings, trying to imagine this castle, in its holiday days in Lusignan times, sieges over, what, he wondered did they do all day in those steep heights? Play chess? Sing? Gamble? Or just gossip away the hours between feasts? The view had been worth the climb, for he could see the faint line of the Turkish mainland and a map-like spread of curving indentations down the island coast to the east, the ridge of rocky hills running to the west, with pine and scrub, dull now, but probably in spring a mass of small flowers. He stayed up there for nearly half an hour, day dreaming in a vague way which was, for him, so often the way a poem began. It seemed as if thoughts which had been drifting suddenly started to take shape, like volcanic islands coming to the sea's surface. At least that was as nearly as he could describe the process. He wrote about three lines on the first page of his little note book, and then strolled down to join Alice, who had been reading the guidebook as she drank her lemonade.

"It's rather awful, but it is cold," she said. "I should think you'd need it. You look boiling. Was it worth the climb?"

"Yes. I'm sorry I was so long, but I felt that as I had got there I'd better look at it properly. Sometimes I do wish I was a painter."

"That's what Maria said." She was surprised, for thinking about it, she realised that she herself was satisfied by the enjoyment of looking without any desire to capture or to recreate what she saw. But it was too hot to give this more than a moment's thought.

"It's pretty good from here." Alice sounded contented. "I've been wondering when the Turks were living here if they wore those shoes with turned up toes, and if the fashion for those long, thin pointed shoes ever got here, and if so, how they all managed those steps everywhere. In fact any stairs must have been murder in those. And long dresses can't have been exactly easy, either."

"How little one knows about all those everyday details, particularly clothes. I should have hated to wear those huge stiff collars that one sees in old photographs."

"I think I'd have enjoyed tall pointed hats with veils but I'd have liked Romney muslins best of all." They finished their lemonade, and returned through vaulted passages, by huge water-tanks where lizards basked, and down to the car. The best memory came from later in the day. They had walked along at the edge of a beach, not a very attractive one, but the sunset colours were beginning. Then Alice said, "Look, look." She was excited, finding a thick-stemmed, ragged-petalled, white flower growing in the sand.

"Goodness. What on earth is it?"

"I don't know. It looks improbable." She knelt to examine it, untidy strap-shaped leaves, several long flower buds, saying, "I didn't think that there'd be any flowers at this time of year, so I didn't bring the flower book."

She got up, and they climbed off the beach, which was rocky now and slippery, into a neglected rough field.

There was another clump of flowers.

"I wish I could bring myself to pick one, but I don't think I should."

At that moment they heard someone whistling and looked up. Two young men were coming towards them, one they recognised, for they had bought a bag of green figs from him a day or two earlier.

The other, obviously a younger brother, was carrying two stems of the white flowers.

"Hullo," said Francis. "No figs today?"

"No. Those were the last." They talked for a few minutes. Both Alice and Francis had been struck by the elder boy's eyes. He was not very tall, his face and arms were a pale even brown and his eyes the green of inshore sea.

Alice turned to the younger boy.

"What do you call these flowers?" she asked.

"No name," he said, then he held them out to her. "For you."

"But didn't you pick them for someone?"

"For you," he repeated.

Alice wanted them very badly, but hesitated still, so he stepped forward and held them out to her.

It was a very vivid memory. The light was fading, and the ridge of hills just inland was almost black against a sunset sky, and Alice in her pink dress seemed to hold all that was left of the daylight. The boy, a head shorter than she, offered his flowers with a graceful courtesy. It was an oddly classic scene, a moment of total pleasure to his eye.

Afterwards they had all strolled back together to the road, talking, smoking, Francis and Alice asking about where the boys lived, and hearing about the difficulty of getting a good education. The younger one hoped to be a doctor, he said, to go to Istanbul to study. But the memory of sea and sunset, the great dragon-backed ridge of dark hills and the crimson sky, and Alice with her white flowers was a visual memory he would not forget. Later, when they came back to their room at bedtime, it was filled with scent. Two of the long buds had opened above the flowers they had left in bloom, and the new flowers were trumpet-shaped below a frilly collar of petals, perfect and not tattered by wind or spray. Another bud showed long green veins from tip to calyx.

"Goodness. I do wonder what it is? I've never seen anything like it, or smelt anything like it either. It's like a lily, but not quite like."

"Could you draw it? Then we could look it up when we get home."
"I'll try, tomorrow."

Later, half asleep, Francis said, "That must be the magic flower
Hermes brought to Ulysses on Circe's island. I never believed it was
an allium."

"But all the garlics are magic, aren't they?" Alice was still wide awake
wondering how such a flower could grow in sand.

But Francis, pleased with his thought of Circe's island, and Alice and
the boy with his flowers, had gone to sleep.

Chapter 10

"Back to time and newspapers and letters," Francis said as they sat in their taxi.

"And the cats."

"I suppose Maria will still be there?"

"I told her what time we'd arrive, and left it to her."

But when Francis opened the door it was Lalla and Tom they found in the hall.

Alice looked at Francis.

"Stella?" They spoke at once.

"Yes." It was Lalla who answered. Tom was carrying in the luggage.

"Let's go and sit down." Alice led the way into the kitchen. She could not help glancing through the window to the garden, though she turned immediately to Lalla.

"It was very strange," Lalla said. "She died yesterday. I was with her, because Terence telephoned to Mrs. Miles and she sent me there at once, and of course her doctor. She told Terence that she didn't want to get up yesterday morning, so he asked the doctor to come, and then I arrived. She was looking very grey and very tired, and I sat on the bed beside her, and so did Terence, and she said, "I can't do any more, I don't think I can finish it." Then she sort of shook all over and opened her eyes and looked at Terence, and smiled, and groaned, and then she wasn't there. The doctor was still with us, so we knew."

Tom said that Lalla had telephoned to him, and he and Terence did all the forms and things. He assumed that people of an older generation than his own must have had to deal with such practicalities, so he was not precise. Lalla went on with her story.

"I stayed with her till the men came to take her away. It was so strange. She looked much smaller, and different; not young, but not old; completed I think. I'd never seen anyone die before, or anyone dead. So I was glad it was Dame Stella. It wasn't frightening at all."

Tom explained that he had telephoned to Maria to find out when they were expected and that she had said it would be much better if he and Lalla would come to break the news, and that she would move out. She was going away, almost immediately, anyway, she said.

"The papers were full of obits, and there was a bit on the news too. But we thought that you probably hadn't heard, so here we are. And we got all the papers for you."

"Bless you both. What about Terence?"

"Oh, Mrs. Miles asked him if he'd like to come to Marion's; he said not, so he's staying with us."

"I'm sorry you had to come home to this," Tom said.

"It always changes reality. I'm afraid that we left everyone's problems behind us, and expected to find everything and everyone where we last saw them." Alice sounded apologetic.

Francis had fetched glasses and poured out gin and tonic for the four of them. Mechanically Alice got ice out of the fridge. She was, she was ashamed to acknowledge, feeling that one problem was solved. She had foreseen a time when Stella would not be able to go on living in her flat, and she had dreaded the decisions that would have to be made with her and for her. She felt that a load had been lifted from her own life.

"Is there anyone who can look after her affairs?" Francis was imagining that Alice might find herself the executor and practical problems would abound.

"That was amazing. She'd told Terence a couple of days ago that if she died, he was to open her desk and there were addresses of lawyers. And did you know, she has a brother?"

"No".

"She told Terence that he was to be sent for and that she'd left instructions. 'It'll really annoy him,' she said. Terence said that she gave him a brisk run down of how tiresome he is, and how much he doesn't like music. But, as he believed that blood is thicker than water he'd have to prove it by dealing with her will. It seemed to amuse her."

Francis was vastly relieved by this news.

"I do thank you for being here, Lalla dear, and you, Tom. It's wonderful to know exactly what happened."

Then, suddenly remembering that Lalla and Tom had had a major, and probably exhausting, experience, Alice went on. "Are you frightfully tired? Seeing death seems to do that to one, as if one had been stretched to an extraordinary limit."

"It was like that. But I was glad to be there, and to sit with her afterwards. I am so sorry for Terence though. He really loved her, and he's so young, he felt both safe with her, and protective, and it's all swept away. We were all talking for half the night."

"What about this evening?" Francis wondered if he ought to ask them all to go out to dinner.

"Oh. We're taking Terence with us to some friends. He's much better today, and he doesn't mind sleeping in our sitting room. He's a sleeping-bag sort of person. And we've got very fond of him."

"Anyway," Tom added. "I expect that you're pretty tired and you'll want to unpack. So we'll be off. Oh yes, and your friend left a note for you." He went into the hall and brought back an envelope.

"Thank you for everything." Alice kissed them both and, her arm round Lalla's shoulder, she said, "I'm so glad you and Tom are together."

Francis saw them off and came back followed by both cats.

"Well, things aren't the same."

"I'm afraid that I feel relieved, but for her as much as for myself. It couldn't have gone on like that much longer. And you were right about that goodbye telephone talk. I'm glad of all she said, and for her that she said it."

"It was a funny little Indian summer. A sort of final picnic. And Terence was absolutely the right companion for it."

"As good a note to end on as any other." Amy was sitting on Alice's lap, and purring. Very comforting, Alice thought, stroking her.

"Another drink please, love. Let's see what Maria has to say."

She read the half page and passed it to Francis. He took it from her. Maria had flamboyant writing.

"I thought it better to go back to the flat. Don't want to be involved in this dénouement. Your young friends were charming and helpful. I think all is well with cats, house and garden. There's a cold chicken and some salad in the fridge, and champagne; reviver, not celebration I suppose. I'm going to Paris for a week, new development, will ring on return. Love Maria."

"Is she bowing out, too?" Alice felt that life was simplifying itself in every direction.

"Do you want to unpack? Tom seems to have carried the luggage upstairs."

"No. Tomorrow will do. Bath? Then dinner?"

"Yes."

"God I'm tired." Alice kicked off her shoes. "I didn't know how tired till they went."

Francis woke early next morning. Alice was still drowned in sleep. They had talked for far longer than they'd meant to after they'd had their chicken and the champagne had made them feel very much awake. They had talked of Stella. News of her death had broken the pattern established through the last months, during which she had become so much a part of their lives. There was a looking back, the inevitable 'if only', and the, as inevitable, contradiction of that to each other, 'but you did'. Then, and more curiously, the realisation of how much they had not known about her. She had been close to their lives for a short time, engrossingly close, but in spite of her talk of friendship, Francis particularly felt that her death emphasized the closing of what must have been a very small chapter of her life.

He opened the drawer in his desk where he kept his work in progress and got out the series of poems on which he'd been working, his poems of old age. He, like other poets who have written about this subject from a distance, was imagining and observing. He had had models as a painter has, but however well he knew them, as Rembrandt must have known his older sitters, he was still imagining what it must be like to have most of life behind, to have achieved or to have missed achievement, and to know that there are no more chances. He had to try to discover how it would feel to be at the mercy of a body that was less a servant than a master.

Stirred by the vivid memory Stella left in his mind, he found that a series of words was there, sharpened by an emotion he had not realised he would feel for her.

When Alice started her day, Stella was her preoccupation too. She went to Marion's of course, and talked again with Lalla and Tom. Stella's brother crossed their lives. He was much younger than she, a successful businessman who collected pictures, charming, helpful, who had been, it appeared, very much in awe of Stella. He was capable,

439

and far less daunted by the complications of her affairs than he had expected to be when she had told him that he was to be her executor. Her famous overdraft, excuse or reason for so many bottles of champagne during her lifetime, was nothing like so dramatic as she had suggested. She had left few personal bequests, all in a recently added codicil. To Francis she had left her manuscript of her settings of his poems. To Terence a thousand pounds and a small Matthew Smith still-life. To Lalla, three Georgian rings that had been in her bank since she had been unable to wear them. And to Alice a delicate twisted gold bracelet with a garnet clasp.

"What a long summer," Alice said. "It's extraordinary how one gets tossed into the middle of all these dramas, and they fill up all the foreground of every day, and then suddenly disappear."

"I'm glad to have you back," Francis answered. "Sometimes I thought that you were living all their lives as well as your own, and your own is the one that matters."

"I know. I felt it too, it was like having the house full of other people all the time, but Stella and Lalla and Tom were all important parts of the story. Maria too, only, that was curious wasn't it? That link with Stella? But Maria and I have lost the sort of friendship we had when we were young. We've become quite different people in all these years, and it's not been one of the friendships that 'picks up where it left off', the kind people talk about so often. Perhaps that does happen sometimes, but perhaps they're more static people?"

"That's certainly not a word I'd use about you or about Maria."

"But I think that, whatever happens to them, I'll always feel glad to see Lalla and Tom."

"They're young, and it's different, perhaps like seeing trees grow?"

"Congenial trees?" Alice said, excluding Maria.

While all these affairs were being sorted out, Maria, after a longer stay than her hastily written note had suggested, came back from Paris and came to see Francis and Alice one afternoon.

"I'm putting my furniture into store for a year," she said. "I'm going to stay in Paris. It's exciting. Two books to translate, and it is something I can do well. It's the most strengthening thing that has ever happened to me."

"What sort of books?" Francis asked her.

"One is a history of tapestries, absolutely fascinating, the language is technical sometimes, but it is all involved with history and costume and dyeing as well as who the workers were and the designers; absolutely pleasurable." She was so obviously excited by the prospect that Alice was interested by her enthusiasm.

"But won't that take you ages?"

"Quite a time, but I don't have to do the research. It has all been done, I just have to catch the writer's style and to do my best to find English to match his French."

"What is the other one?"

"Some rather sinister fairy stories. The two seem to go together in an odd way, in fact we're going to use pictures of some of the tapestries to illustrate the stories."

"The same author, then?" Francis asked.

"Yes."

"Oh Maria, I am so glad," Alice was burning with curiosity and managing not to ask for more information than Maria offered. "This does sound like the beginning of a new chapter."

"It's the beginning of proper work. I think that is what has been wrong with me for ages. Not having to concentrate except when I felt like it."

"The dreaded mastery of deadlines?" Francis teased.

"Yes." She took the question seriously. "And I shall learn such a lot of history in the process."

"What about Russian?"

"There'll be time for that, too. It's incredibly lucky, Jean-Paul's mother was Russian and it is his second language."

"Your bread buttered on both sides'?" Maria looked at Alice, who was smiling.

"Do you know, it just might be that, I don't know, yet. I'll tell you in a year and a day. Fairy stories, even the sinister ones, or perhaps those most of all, measure time in a different way from calendars and timetables, and I'm catching the habit. But, meanwhile, I think that I can start quite a different kind of life." She was serious as well as excited.

"I'm suddenly grateful to that awful Désirée. Paris, instead of Australia, Francis, and proper work, and - well, we'll see."

"Where will you live?"

"That's settled too. I'll give you my address, I can't believe how it's all worked out - so far."

When she left, Francis walked a little way down the road with her.

"You came like a comet", he said, "and now you go off into what? An enchanted forest? A pavilion guarded by unicorns?"

"Actually a part of a flat in the Marais; I can't talk about it yet, but I wanted you to know."

They had been walking slowly. She stopped and turned to him.

"It all began for me that day." She didn't have to explain which day. "Because I realised, with you, that so much had been all wrong for me with Charles. I didn't know it at once, in fact not till this happened. But I think that day was the beginning"

Francis had an unexpected sharp instant of jealousy, an instant of precise memory, that he knew she shared.

"Goodbye, Maria. The appropriate thing is, to wish that your three wishes are granted."

"My...three wishes? Yes, but those usually left people where they were before, disappointed and cross, didn't they? One will do, this time."

"Send me your books."

"Of course. Thank you Francis."

They kissed each other, formally, and he said, "Thank you, Beauty."

They parted on that echo, and Francis walked home very slowly, remembering his first recognition, 'Oh she was a fire-ship.' He had half of a remembered tune in his head as well as a half recollection of the words, 'and then she sailed away.'

"And just as well, just as well she did," he thought, "because I'd much rather live with Alice."

It was quite a long time after Stella's death before there was a memorial concert. It was at the Wigmore Hall, and the audience was very largely of young people to whom she had suddenly become a cult figure. Francis and Alice were there, as were Lalla and Tom and Terence. They, except for Terence, knew very few of the other people, though the hall was full. The mirror poems were sung by a girl they did not know; there were two string quartets and, at the end, the work which she had somehow completed in the last weeks of her life, the

one she had written partly at Marion's, partly afterwards, while
Terence looked after her. This was for oboe, viola and 'cello. It was
written in a musical language unfamiliar to Francis. But as he listened
he remembered his talk with her about death, and thought that he
understood from where the essence of the music came. He felt that
he was listening to meaning beyond unfamiliar means of expression. It
gave him the final poem for his sequence, and it came not only from
her music but from the dream he had told her during the summer:

> Bastions of rock were certainly a city
> unlit and distant on the cliffs of night,
> clouds, defined by movement, blowing
> above a plain of lesser stones and boulders
> where fear should have inhabited with space and silence.
> I was alone, clothed in exaltation
> as if all wishes and all hopes were found,
> as if, in that wide darkness, I was light.